MALIBU

THE WOMAN'S GOURMET SEX BOOK

BY PEGGY & EVAN BURKE

THE WOMAN'S GOURMET SEX BOOK

BY PEGGY & EVAN BURKE

"There will no man do for your sake,
                              I think,
What I would have done for the
                              least word said.
I have wrung life dry for your lips
                              to drink,
Broken it up for your daily
                              bread."

Swinburne, **The Triumph of Time**

INTRODUCTION

The Woman's Gourmet Sex Book is unlike any book you have seen. It is a book for the woman who wishes to give the fullest romantic and sexual satisfaction to the man (or men) in her life, and who realizes that by doing so she gains the highest degree of satisfaction for herself.

This day-by-day guide to the development of sensuality will fire the imagination of the female whose long-standing relationship with one man has become tarnished by repetition; and the woman who enjoys a casual relationship with a man will discover that her new awareness opens new avenues of pleasure for the two of them.

The Gourmet Sex Book is going to show you how to make a man feel unique. It is going to show you how to convince him that he — and only he — is so special that he receives your very special attentions.

And *you* are going to reap the rewards.

Your new sensuality, and the sexual prowess you are going to acquire in the months ahead, will bring new vigor to the romantic efforts of your man. As you apply the techniques presented in this book, as your lovemaking grows delightfully varied, his own imagination will be triggered, and he will begin to seek new ways of pleasing you.

If you are married, or if there is a steady man in your life, you may wish to give him *The Man's Gourmet Sex Book*. This companion book tells the man all he needs to know in order to please you; and it passes along secrets about female sexuality that you, yourself, may not be aware of, while also suggesting delightful ways of using them.

But *The Woman's Gourmet Sex Book* is not just another "sex manual." While imparting knowledge about the male anatomy and desires, and describing numerous ways in which you may use this knowledge to stimulate your man and drive him to new heights of abandon, it does so without reducing sex to a mechanical act or a list of statistics. You will find that this book is filled with suggestions on sexual positions and erotic techniques. But it should be remembered that they are only suggestions and nothing more. You may find that some of them are not to your liking, some may violate your own personal code of moral ethics, and your inhibitions may be too strong to allow you to engage in others. That is all well and good. These words were not handed down from the mountain on tablets of stone, and it is your right to reject any of them.

You will soon find that certain types of sexual activity are especially appealing to you, to your man, or to the two of you. As new vistas are opened to you through your use of *The Gourmet Sex Book,* you will certainly wish to delve deeper into the areas which please you, creating your own variations as you go. Enjoy yourself, but try not to fall into a pattern that excludes other exploration. Patterns lead only to boredom, and boredom is the death of things.

Not all the entries in this book are sexual in nature, but all will add something of value to the relationship between you and your man. Sex and love — or at least affection — are inseparable, and these expressions of love are going to show that you care about him as person. Such expressions are important to a man. They bolster his ego and strengthen his feelings of masculinity. They are the small touches that may transform the casual affair into an enduring romance.

It is suggested that you do not make a thorough study of *The Gourmet Sex Book* before you are ready to put it to use. Allow yourself to enjoy the element of surprise as, on each day of the year that lies ahead, you turn a new page to discover the treat that is in store for you.

Refer to the guide several hours before you expect to be with your man. Carefully read the entry for that date, letting your imagination roam freely and try to create vivid images of what lies ahead. Think of your own variations on this day's suggestion. Can you add a personal touch of improvement? If you can, you have taken a giant step toward total sexual fulfillment.

Your excitement and enthusiasm will increase as your mind dwells on the forthcoming experience; and later, when the two of you are together, you will receive an added bonus as your ardor is transmitted to him. Nothing is more arousing to a man than a woman who is trembling with eagerness. Let that woman be *you!*

Begin with the present date. *The Gourmet Sex Book* is arranged so that it has no beginning and no end. Any page of the book is the starting point for a new year of sexual happiness. At the end of that year, you are going to be a new woman; desired as never before, fulfilled as never before, and you will have enjoyed each movement spent in the transformation.

Happy loving!

January 1

Happy New Year!

But how was the old one? Ask yourself that question and answer it honestly. If it was not the best year possible, now is the time to plan improvement.

You know how you thrill to the touch of his lips and tongue as he caresses those sensitive places, but have you taken extra care with your personal hygiene? No man is going to warn you about *that*. Be certain you are on safe ground here, and, if you have the slightest doubt, don't be afraid to try one of the scented feminine sprays. Special care in this area is likely to receive an oral award—and that doesn't mean he will talk about it!

Have you always presented yourself at your best? During the year that begins today—let it be resolved!—he is not going to see you with your hair in curlers, with your lovely body hidden beneath a formless housecoat, or with your feet in those floppy slippers you have long intended to throw away. He is going to see only the sexy, desirable creature that is you—and he is going to see you at your luscious best.

Neither is your loving going to be lazy and only grudgingly given. It is going to be entered into with enthusiasm for the joyous act that it is, and with each new experience there will be improvement.

Let these be among your resolutions.

January 2

Go shopping for lingerie today.

In most large cities there are specialty shops which carry a wide line of extremely sexy feminine apparel. Try to find one of these, as they offer a huge assortment of imaginative undergarments designed to stimulate the erotic interests of men. Here you will find leather skirts and peek-a-boo blouses, cutaway bras, and crotchless panties—everything needed to drive a man wild. Go to a department store if you must, where the selection is usually smaller, but be selective and choose items that accent your beauty. Black is delightful in contrast to the light coloring of most blondes. If your skin is tawny, you may want

9

to try something in white, red, or any of the brighter colors. Redheads usually look their best in green or blue.

Even if he is paying the bill, this is one shopping spree to which your man is not going to object. You will know you have chosen well when you see the fire in his eyes as he takes you in his arms to strip you naked—which was, after all, the purpose of this little shopping trip.

But say nothing to him about it in advance. Let him make this pleasant discovery for himself. Showered and perfumed, your hair brushed to shining perfection, slip into the most exciting outfit you have chosen. Put the rest away and say nothing about them; they are going to be brought out, piece by exciting piece, as delicious surprises in the future.

Cover your scantily-clad body with the thinnest, most attractive lounging robe you own, and let your desire for him be evident when you meet him at the door. Take his hands and draw his arms around your waist as you step close to him and kiss him passionately on the lips.

No man can resist a woman who is so eager to be with *him*.

This will become clear as he reacts with caresses of his own, caresses that are certain to continue until you are standing before him with his hands stripping away your oh-so-sexy bra and panties, while his lips emit a low whistle of appreciation. His appreciation of your new loveliness will be even more obvious when his own clothes are shed.

What follows will be worth every dime you spent.

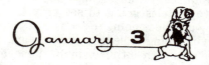

January **3**

Tonight you are going to show him that beauty is not all you have to offer. You are going to give him a sexual experience that will linger in his memory for months to come, just as it will linger in your own!

When the foreplay has advanced to a point where further delay is unbearable, and his hands have stripped away your clothing, indicate to him that you wish to be entered from behind. You need not put this desire into words; his excitement will be far greater if you take the initiative and guide him there with your hands.

You may wish to try this while standing, your legs slightly spread, and bending forward at the waist to rest your hands on the edge of the bed or a chair; or it may be done while on your side, with him behind you. The rear entry is the important thing.

Now for the something special that makes this such a treat.

Men crave a woman who is "tight." That is the extra friction against the penis that is caused by the tightly clinging walls of a small vagina which gives an added degree of pleasure, and you are now going to give him a delicious friction beyond any he has known.

As his hard penis enters you, reach down and press the fingers of one hand against the soft mound of flesh above your vagina. This is the *mons* area, sometimes called the "mound of Venus," and he will feel a new pressure as you push against it. Move your fingers in slow circles, allowing yourself the added pleasure of a few touches on your clitoral flesh, and you will soon feel his unquestionably heated reaction.

Now let your hand move a little lower. Close the thumb and forefinger over your labia, the outer lips of your vagina. They will be distended around his penis and easy to grasp. With your hips rolling and your bodily undulations never slowing, allow your fingers to open and close over your labia. He will feel the results of each delicate squeeze, and you may soon feel his hand leaving your breast to slip down and assist the movements of your fingers.

Nothing pleases a man more than the knowledge that a woman is thinking of *his* pleasure. This little trick will lead him to believe just that—even though the pleasure will be equally shared.

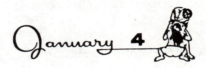

January 4

Spend part of today learning more about your own body—for the woman who truly understands her own body is the one most capable of giving pleasure to her male partner.

Shower and then towel your body—until the skin is glowing and your nipples are firmly erected. Dim the lights in the bedroom, make yourself comfortable, and let your hands make a slow exploration of your naked body. There is no other body exactly like it.

Though all women have certain erogenous zones in common, the intensity of the reaction to a caress bestowed upon these areas will vary from woman to woman. Find the spots that give *you* the greatest pleasure—so you can guide *him* there.

Let your fingers gently stroke your nipples, your *mons* and your clitoris. Lift your hips and touch the tip of your finger to your anus; you may be surprised to find this pleasurable. Many women are excited by anal contact. If you are one of them, let *his* fingers be the next to touch you there—and remember to guide his lips, tongue, and even his penis to those other spots you found especially exciting.

His excitement will surpass your own.

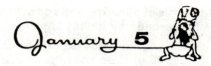

January 5

What about cunnilingus? Does the man in your life often drop to his knees before you, or turn on the bed beside you, to orally caress your clitoris until you are thrashing with repeated orgasms? Or has he never done this?

If your man has done this before—either regularly or only occasionally—show your pleasure by encouraging him to repeat the act tonight. Give him the encouragement silently, by using your hands to guide his kisses from your lips to your neck to your breasts, then to their final, delightful resting place. He will enjoy this all the more because *you* wanted him to do it.

Your man may be too shy to try oral techniques, or he may feel—foolish man!—that you would be offended by any such attempt. While the same body language described above will get the message across to this type of lover, turning on the bed beside him and placing your vagina conveniently near his face while you orally caress him is by far the most effective encouragement you can give.

January 6

You know that variety is the spice of sex, and you know that a new position is one way of providing that variety. But why not try a slight change of location? Tonight you are going to use the bedroom for sleeping—or for a second round of love!

Meet him at the door wearing something sexy; and be quick to let him know you are in a passionate mood. Then, when he makes his first amorous move, whether it be in the kitchen, the bath, or the hall, let him know that this is the spot, this is the time.

Remove your panties, or let him remove them, but don't bother with the rest of your clothing. Urgency is the name of the game tonight, and you may discover that *his* sense of urgency remains constant into the wee hours of morning.

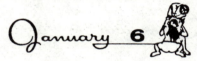

January 7

This is the day for an exercise that will greatly increase your sensuality and your ability to orally stimulate him beyond his wildest dreams. This series of exercises will, by giving your tongue a new strenth and flexibility, make your kisses more potent, your fellatio more exciting. Start your practice today and repeat it regularly.

1. Move your tongue in a slow, circular motion around your lips, wetting them. Move the tongue clockwise several times, then counterclockwise, trying always to extend it farther.

2. Extend your tongue as far as possible, then move it up and down in a flickering motion.

3. Try to touch your nose with your tongue.

4. Try to touch your chin.

5. With your tongue fully extended, move it slowly from side to side, then draw it back into your mouth. Repeat this several times, or until you get tired.

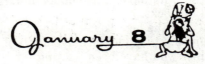

January 8

Today, while you are alone, make up a very special set of checkers. Using a regular set of checkers, and writing with a ballpoint pen, mark each of the red checkers with the name of an item of male clothing; list your garments on the black checkers.

Challenge him to a game of "strip-checkers." The rules of the game are simple: when you jump a red checker marked "shirt," for instance, that is what he must remove. If you lose a black checker to him, you remove the matching item of your own clothing.

The game can be made more interesting by selecting, before play begins, a penalty to be paid by the loser. You choose his penalty; he selects yours. Choose the penalties properly and this will be a game which nobody loses.

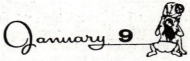

January 9

Be a brazen hussy today!

Shortly before he is due to go on his lunch break, give him a call at work. In a husky whisper tell him how you have been thinking of him, needing him, and describe what would take place if only you were together. One of two things will occur.

If time permits, he will come rushing to you, excited and almost breathless—but not too breathless for love. If distance makes this impossible, he will spend the day thinking about that call, his excitement growing as the hours pass, and he will be a bundle of sexual energy when at last he comes rushing to your arms. In either case, the day will become a memorable one.

January 10

Many of those flourishing massage parlors offer more than a massage, and you can offer the same to your man. Buy one of those flat vibrators that are made to strap on the back of the hand; they are fairly inexpensive.

Wear a short, belted kimono if you have one, and be sure to wear nothing beneath it. Let him have ample opportunity to glimpse your breasts, thighs, and buttocks.

Have him lie naked on the bed as you begin the massage. You will soon find him reaching out to guide the movements of your hands, and this is the signal which you have been waiting for.

Let the fingers of the hand wearing the vibrator close around his erected penis and, moving them slowly, touch your lips to the tip of his shaft. Put your tongue to work, using all the movements you know, and go just as far as you like. The tingling caress of your fingers will lift him to a new peak of arousal, and the odds are good that he soon will be using that vibrator on *you*.

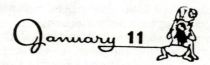

January 11

Men are subject to varying degrees of anal eroticism, and you should know exactly how your man responds to this type of stimulation. Too many men believe, incorrectly, that only homosexuals derive pleasure from anal contact, so you are not going to ask how he feels about the subject. You are going to find the answer by seeing how he responds.

As you begin to make love, guide him over you and into the male-dominant position. Then, while he caresses you and fondles your breasts, let your hands move to his buttocks. Keep your body in motion, your hips rolling, and gently spread his buttocks.

Still no objection? Fine.

Being careful of your nails, touch the flat underside of one finger to his anus. If he still makes no objection, apply a gentle pressure, maintaining it until the tip of your invading finger is inside him.

You are likely to find yourself being rewarded by a quickened and

14

lengthened driving of his hips that will provide the ultimate in pleasure for the two of you.

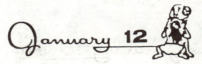

January 12

You are going to become a call girl!

Of course, it is against the law to charge for your sexual favors, which you would never dream of doing, so you are merely going to pretend.

Make a list of your prices—so much for "straight" sex, so much for oral sex, etc.—and give the list to him. Tell him, in your most serious voice, that you now charge and these are your rates.

Then give him a small stack of play money and let him spend it.

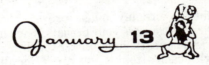

January 13

You know he is excited by your breasts, that he loves to squeeze and stroke them, that he often tastes of your erected nipples. But have you given him all the pleasure your breasts have to offer?

Have him lie on his back, naked. Kneel beside him and, cupping your breasts in your hands, offer each in turn to his mouth. Allow him to suck them for a long moment before moving on.

And as you move on, still kneeling so the tips of your breasts sway against his body, you will see his penis grow erect. Let your stiff nipples tease his chest, his stomach, his thighs, and then take his erection in your hand and tease the tip of it with your nipples.

You will have one totally aroused male on your hands.

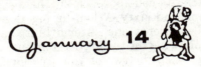

January 14

Give him a truly erotic display!

Have him lie on his back, his legs together, while you—wearing only a garter belt and sexy nylons—straddle his body with your face toward his feet.

This position allows him to see the enticing flesh of your vaginal lips as they settle over his penis, and it allows him to follow your body as you begin to move above him. You can give him an even better view by leaning far forward, and your efforts will be rewarded when you feel the magnificent growth of his erection inside you.

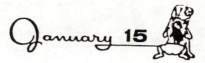

January 15

Do you recall the girl in your school who had the reputation of being a tease? She wore the shortest skirts, the tightest sweaters, and she promised the most but delivered the least. She might allow the boys to paw her breasts, or slip a trembling finger beneath the elastic of her panties, but that was as far as she went. And the fellows loved her for it!

That is because men love a challenge, love chasing the unattainable. So tonight you are going to be a tease—but you are going to be a tease who delivers.

Act as if you want the foreplay to last forever. Find some excuse to break away when first he touches your breasts. Then let it resume until he tries to slip his hand beneath your skirt. Stop him again. Allow a little more freedom with each attempt (you are, after all, unable to resist him), then, when he 7s hot, hard and ready, allow your resistance to melt like April snow.

You have been seduced!

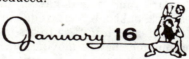

January 16

Take him to see a naughty movie—one that is rated R or X. He will be aroused by the scenes he witnesses there, but it will be nothing compared to the excitement caused by the surprise you have planned.

Take along a watch. As you approach the theater, ask him to pick a number between one and sixty. When he has done so, picking, for example, the number twenty-one, inform him that the first erotic thing said or done following the twenty-first minute of the movie is going to be duplicated when the two of you are alone.

He will be on the edge of his seat until the selected moment arrives.

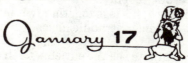

January 17

You are going to seduce *him*. Meet him at the door, your body encased in your sexiest outfit, and tell him exactly what you are going to do, adding that you want him to resist for as long as he can. Then put all your skills to work.

Let your hands roam his body, your tongue explore his mouth. Remove his shirt and toy with his nipples, just as he would do with yours. Try biting them gently. You will find that they stiffen in the same manner as your own. And he will soon begin to weaken, just as you knew he would.

The passive role will be a unique experience for him, one that will thrill him in special ways, and you will soon find that he has become anything but passive.

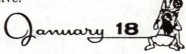

Challenge him to a contest of wills.

Undress and select a coital position that allows him to enter you from the front. This gives each of you an equal chance in the contest that is to follow. After he has entered you, when the two of you are locked in close embrace, see who can refrain from moving the pelvis for the longest time.

He is allowed to kiss and stroke you, and you are allowed to do the same to him. The first to make a copulatory motion loses.

But both of you will win.

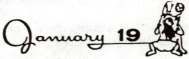

Men love the feel of silk or nylon against their naked skin. That is why he is wild about those shimmering bits of wispy underthings you wear to excite him. So use them to excite him even more.

Remove your panties and fold them into a silken pad in the palm of your hand. Slowly rub the pad over his testicles, letting your hand move close to the cleft between his buttocks; and then, as he begins to move, make a fist around his penis. The sleek material of the panties will add a special thrill to those caused by the manipulations of your moving fingers, and you may add even more by bending down to cover his penis with your parted lips. He will be rising to meet you.

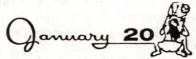

Did you know many men like a tiny bit of pain along with their sex? It is true, but be careful not to overdo it.

Try nipping at the lobes of his ears, at his neck, and at his nipples, while easing the pain by using your fingers to stroke his penis and testicles. He may urge you to nibble gently at the fleshy parts of his male organ, which should be done with extreme caution as it is very sensitive to pain.

With no panties and no bra, wear a tightly clinging outfit with an extremely short skirt. Pretend to be unaware of the way your skirt lifts to reveal your buttocks and a tempting glimpse of pubic hair as you move about the room, casually bending now and then to perform some needless chore. Be happily shocked when you feel his hand or his lips against your naked flesh.

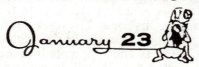

Be a lady in the parlor, a harlot in the bedroom.

Tonight, no matter what your mood, be a little bit aloof, a lady who is not the least bit interested in sex—until the moment you enter your bedroom!

Then, using the most unladylike language of which you are capable, descirbe to him the sensations you feel as he caresses your breasts, *mons*, and clitoris. Tell him how you love the touch of his tongue. Let him know how you thrill to the thrusting of his penis. Compliment him on his skills, his endurance, and his incredible size.

Men love this, as it plays upon the male ego, and you are likely to find his bedroom skills increasing as you put the technique to use. It is one form of oral stimulation you give without taking him into your mouth!

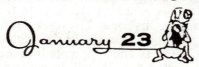

Did you know that men very often make love to one woman while imagining they are with another? Or that they are doing it in a different way, or a different place, or a unique position? You may think this sad, but it is true.

Create a fantasy of your own. Make it something he would never expect of you. Then tonight, in those lazy moments following love, when a man will reveal his innermost thoughts, describe—in vivid detail—

your fantasy. Encourage him to talk about his. You may find they are more bizarre than you expected, and some of them may disagree with your tastes. But others will excite you, and you might want to please him by acting these out. In any case, you will have learned a great deal about what excites your man.

January 24

You know that fellatio sends him into ecstasy. You know he would go wild if you took all of his penis into your mouth, but your attempts to do so cause you to gag. You can overcome this.

The trick is in learning to breathe properly. You can learn to do so by using a peeled banana as a substitute for him. Take it into your mouth and slide it as deep as possible, then withdraw it. Breathe in through your nose while only the tip of the banana is in your mouth, then exhale as you begin to slide it deep. You will find that throwing your head back causes the muscles of the upper throat to relax and open, allowing even deeper thrusts. Begin this excercise in sensuality today and practice it often.

January 25

Do you recall, from your days as a teen-ager, the excitement of necking and engaging in heavy petting at a drive-in movie? Of course you do. And much of that excitement was caused by the knowledge that you could not, as the teens put it, "go all the way."

So have him take you to a drive-in theater. Sit in the back seat of the car. Go just as far as the law and the proximity of the other cars will allow. Somewhere around the middle of the first reel, you will be leaving the theater, your man in a state of red-hot readiness he will carry with him into the bedroom.

January 26

Did you know you can use a few cubes of ice to give a man the most intense orgasm he has ever known? It is a delightfully simple and tremendously effective piece of sexual artistry.

Have a container of ice within easy reach. Let him suspect that you are going to use it, but be sure not to tell him how. Use all your oral techniques to bring him to the brink of orgasm.

Then, just as the tremendous pulsations in his erected penis tell you he is about to erupt, take some ice and place it quickly against his testicles.

And be ready to witness the greatest orgasm of his life!

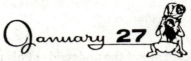

January **27**

Add a little variety to your lovemaking by placing yourself over him in the female-dominant position. *He* likes this position because it makes it so much easier for him to suck and lick your breasts, and *you* will love the way it allows you to control the pace of the action.

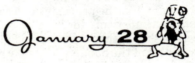

January **28**

Be a centerfold girl!

With a Polaroid camera and the help of a friend (female, of course) take several photographs of yourself. Make them as sexy as possible, and paste them over the centerfold page of the latest issue of his favorite male-interest magazine.

Then relax and wait for his reaction when he discovers them.

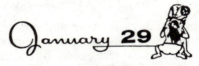

January **29**

List your ten favorite ways of making love. Put them down on paper, so you will not be tempted to cheat later on, and give each method a number. Tell him what you have done, but don't let him see the list.

Just smile and ask him to pick a number!

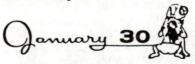

January **30**

This is the most pleasant exercise in sensuality you are ever going to attempt. That is because you are going to do it with him.

Tonight, as you make love, try to constrict the muscles of your vagina around his penis. Then let them relax. Try to tighten them once again. It may seem difficult at first, but it will become easier as you begin putting those dormant muscles to use.

Now lift your hips and let them weave beneath him. Try to get away from the churning motion most women use. Let your pelvis move in circles, squares and figure-eights, always varying the speed.

A nice way to practice, isn't it!

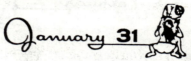

January 31

Running along the length of the underside of his penis is a thick and extremely sensitive tissue ridge that looks very much like a vein. It is the one erogenous zone you can use to excite him most.

Learn about it tonight!

Try teasing it lightly with your fingers. Touch it with the tip of your tongue. By letting your tongue flicker across it as you move down the length of his penis, then back again, you can soon have him shivering in ecstasy; and, by continuing to tease him in this manner—now and then taking the tip of his penis softly between your lips until he explodes in orgasm—you can cause him to end this month as the most completely satisfied man in town.

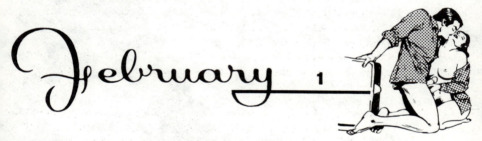

February 1

You can give him a strange but extremely pleasant thrill by making love to him while he is blindfolded. There is something strangely erotic in not knowing where to expect the next kiss or caress. Ask him to let you provide these thrills.

Have him lie on the bed, naked, and give him a glimpse of your own nude body before you put the blindfold in place.

Begin by teasing his body with your fingers. Let them wander over his chest and stomach, his thighs, penis, and testicles. Pause for a moment. Then, using your lips instead of your hands, repeat these caresses. Be sure to let him feel your breasts grazing his naked body. Press your pubic hair against him. Let your tongue touch him in unexpected places.

You can add to his pleasure by not letting him know when or where to expect the next touch of your fingers, lips or tongue, and you can make the night complete by unexpectedly covering him with your mouth and using your oral skills to bring him to climax.

February 2

Happy Groundhog Day!

The shadow plays an important part in the mythology surrounding this day, so let your shadow help you to arouse him.

Rig a light so that it will cast your shadow on the wall in front of his favorite chair. Have the light placed so that he will not be able to see you but will see only the shadow.

Wait until he is comfortably settled, then leave him and turn on the light. Very slowly, standing so that the shadow of your profile is cast upon the wall, begin to do a striptease. Make your movements erotic and sensuous. Let your hands caress your breasts as you remove your bra; let your fingers linger on your thighs as you slip your panties down.

Soon there will be two shadows on the wall.

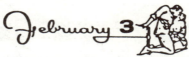

Try combining oral and anal stimulation. It is a combination of erotic sensations most men will love.

Begin by letting your tongue and lips bring his penis to full hardness. Then slowly let your mouth wander to the cleft between his buttocks. He will turn to make your task easier; you may be sure of that!

With the fingers of one hand still teasing his penis and testicles, let your other hand grip his buttocks. Press the flat wetness of your tongue to his flesh, then slowly begin to lick him, the tip of your tongue moving closer to his anus. Then spread his buttocks and touch him there, your tongue flickering.

You will find that by inserting the tip of your tongue into this orifice, or by letting it lap gently against its outer flesh, you can quickly bring him to the brink of orgasm. And covering his penis with your lips will quickly drive him over this brink.

The anus, like most other parts of the human body, is a self-cleaning apparatus. Except at the moment of defecation, it contains only microscopic amounts of fecal matter, so there is really no valid reason for not adding this technique to your sexual arsenal.

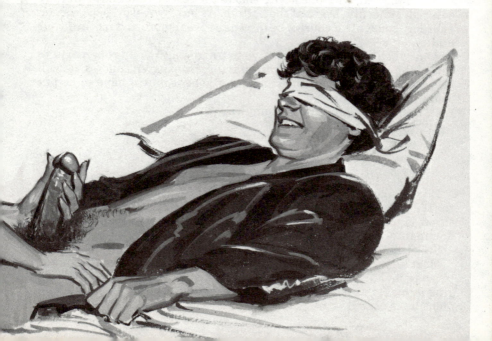

February 4

Try taking a bottle of baby oil to bed with you.

After he has undressed completely, and you have done the same, slowly anoint his body with the lotion. Let your hands move excitingly as you cover his chest, thighs, stomach, and groin with the oil. Then let him apply it to you. You will find yourself growing more and more excited as his hands rub the smooth lotion over your breasts, your legs, and your buttocks.

And as you make love the oil will give a sleek feel to your bodies that must be felt to be understood.

February 5

Meet him at the door wearing a sexy gown, and beneath this gown wear nothing but a set of very, very transparent panties. Tell him you were just shaving your legs, and teasingly ask if he would like to help. He will gladly agree.

Sit on the bed, with one leg extended, the rest of your body carefully covered. Make him begin at the bottom. As he slowly works his way up your leg, you will, of course, be forced to reveal more and more of your nudity.

And when at last he reaches your thighs and your robe parts to reveal the treasure beneath those skimpy, transparent undies, he will become so aroused that the shaving of your legs will have to be put aside till another day.

Of couse they didn't need it anyway.

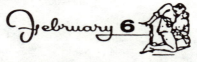

February 6

Do you know why the classic position for fellatio is the one in which the female kneels before the male? It is most probably because this position is one that strengthens the inherent desire of the male to be dominant.

So let him be dominant!

Meet him at the door with excitement in your eyes and, after one or two passionate kisses, lead him to a cozy chair. Let your fingers be tugging at his fly as he seats himself there, and be on your knees the moment he is seated.

Kneeling before him, while he still fights to overcome his surprise, take him quickly and greedily into your mouth and use every delighting trick of fellatio you know.

To surprise your man in such a manner is one of the most arousing things you can do, for it convinces him that he was in your thoughts while away, and leads him to the mistaken belief that he is your sexual master. But in reality this little trick will so increase his desire for you that it will be quite questionable as to who is the dominant partner.

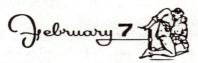

February 7

Have him sit on a chair and watch you as you slowly and seductively strip away your clothing. When your striptease has brought him to full erection, and the erection can be seen thrusting upward against the front of his trousers, pause long enough to open his fly and take it out. Remove the rest of your clothing.

Now slowly move astride him, lowering yourself down over his penis as you lock your lips to his. Open his shirt so he can feel your naked breasts against his chest. Slip your arms around his neck and use this leverage to lift yourself to the tip of his erection, then slowly, ever so slowly, lower yourself to accept it all.

You will soon feel his hands going under your buttocks to assist the rise and fall of your body, and his lips will be seeking the breasts which this position places so conveniently near his face.

You can vary this position by turning in his lap, so that your buttocks are nestled against his groin, your breasts begging to be taken into his hands, and his lips against your naked shoulders and back.

Either way it is a love-position the two of you will love.

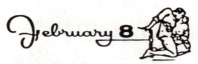

February 8

Ask him to take a shower with you.

But don't be waiting in the shower with your clothing already removed. Let him undress you, and you do the same to him. And let your fingers cover his body with intimate caresses as you strip away his clothing. His will certainly do the same to you.

When you are at last in the shower together, take turns applying the soap. Let him cover your breasts, thighs, buttocks, and pubis with thick lather before you go to work on him. Then, after you have covered his body with suds, let your fingers close tightly over his penis and press your body against his as the spray washes the soap from the two of you.

The size and shape of your shower stall will dictate the position you take during the act that follows, but you will find that the spray of water beating down on your bodies adds a new zest to this clean fun.

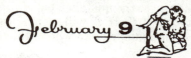

February 9

Become his servant for the night.

Prepare his favorite dinner, then meet him at the door dressed in the typical costume of a maid: a tiny cap, very high heels, a small black apron, sexy hosiery—and nothing else.

Make him suffer through the meal before allowing him to reach out and touch the delicious flesh revealed by your scanty costume. Be sure to move about in a manner that will allow him to glimpse the naked curves of your buttocks, which the costume should reveal, and when he has finally finished the meal, announce that it is time for dessert.

Then take off your apron!

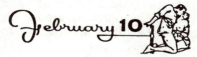

February 10

Using watercolors that are easily removed, challenge him to a creative body-painting contest. The winner is the one who creates the most erotic design on the body of the other.

As the two of you begin your artistic endeavors you will find that the touch of the tiny brushes against your naked flesh creates sensations far more erotic than the designs you are attempting to draw. And the contest will end in a draw when you realize that the most erotic designs are the ones you have on each other, and you settle the matter by bringing your paint-covered bodies together and smearing your artistic creations beyond recognition.

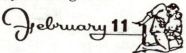

February 11

Tonight, arrange to have him take you out to dinner or to a show. Then, just before it is time to leave, call him to your room and let him find you totally nude. After making it absolutely clear that there is to be no sex—at least for the moment—ask him to help you dress.

As he helps you into your nylons, garter belt, panties, bra and, finally, your dress, you will find him trying to change your mind about

26

the ground rules you have laid down. Be firm in your refusal and insist upon going through with your plans.

You will find that his excitement lingers and increases throughout the evening, and he will eventually insist upon returning home much earlier than you had planned.

Then, in the bedroom, he will eagerly reverse the act you put him through earlier.

Tonight, as you make love, encourage him to explore your anal area. You may be surprised at the degree of excitement this causes.

While you are locked in tight sexual embrace, reach down and draw his hands around to your buttocks. With your fingers over his, encourage him to part these fleshy orbs and then squirm until you feel his finger touch your anus. The same nerves which cause such excitement when your clitoris is touched extend to the area of the anus, and if you are like a great many women, you may find yourself asking him to force that finger deeper through your rear orifice.

Not only can such anal play increase your own sexual pleasure greatly, it also opens up new avenues of exploration for him and helps him become the great lover you want him to be.

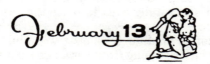

Tonight, shortly before he is due to arrive, go to the privacy of your bedroom and, stripping away your clothing, make yourself comfortable on the bed. Now, forget all the old bugaboos about masturbation—they are invalid in this day and age, and masturbation is a perfectly legitimate means of stimulation.

Let your hands caress the areas of your body that give you pleasure, and fill your mind with vivid sexual images. Use pressure on the soft mound above your vagina and gentle finger-touches on your clitoris to bring yourself to the thin edge of orgasm—then force yourself to stop. Get dressed.

When you meet him at the door the unmistakable glow of desire will still remain on your face, the fire of sexual need will glow in your eyes.

And he will be quick to do something about it.

February 14
Valentine's Day

Valentine's Day—the day of lovers!

Make it a day—or night—of love he will never forget by showing him what a fantastic lover he really is . . . time after time after time.

For this special night you will want to be at your sexy best. Beneath a dress that flatters and reveals your best assets wear a bra that does little to conceal your breasts, and panties that were designed to be removed by a man. Let him remove these at the earliest possible moment.

Although most women have a far greater amount of sexual stamina than their male counterparts, there are many ways in which the knowing woman can arouse the male to repeated orgasm, and that is going to be your gift to him on this day of lovers. And you will be receiving your own gift while in the process of giving.

After the first round of love, as he is still recovering his breath, surprise him by quickly bending over him and taking his softened penis into your mouth. Oral stimulation will usually renew the energy of even the most exhausted male, and you will soon feel the hard results within your mouth. Let him take it from there.

Another excellent way to restore his vigor is to press your naked body against his back, your breasts naked against his skin, your pubic hair teasing his buttocks, and your lips bestowing wet kisses on his shoulders as you reach around to grasp his softened penis. Let your fingers move over him, slowly masturbating him, and you will soon find him aroused and rolling over to place the results between your thighs.

Anal stimulation is another trick that will almost always bring a man to erection. With a teasing finger or an expert touch of the tongue, you can repeatedly bring him to a state of readiness, and the two of you can then enjoy the results.

Use all these methods to prolong your sex on this day of lovers and it will become a never-to-be-forgotten date. No man ever forgets the woman who makes him pleasantly surprise himself.

February 15

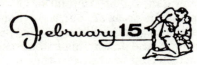

Place a tape recorder beneath your bed. Let it run while the two of you are making love, and say nothing to him about it. Try to forget it yourself, as a matter of fact.

Later, as the two of you are relaxing, tell him what you have done and then play the recording. You are probably going to be surprised at the things you have said while in the throes of passion, and it is more than likely that the erotic sounds pouring from that recorder will soon have the two of you back in bed.

February 16

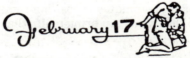

Add a special excitement to the act of cunnilingus.

As the two of you begin to make love, use words or your own special body language to indicate that you want him to make oral love to you. But tonight you are going to make this act unusually appealing to him.

Be on your back, with your thighs parted. As his lips move down over your body toward the target you have indicated, let your fingers do the same. Let them be stroking your vagina by the time his lips arrive there—and let them continue as he begins.

Gently stroke your clitoris and the fleshy hood which surrounds it, exactly as if you were alone and masturbating. Let the seductive rolling of your hips assist the stroking of your fingers.

This combination of visual and other sensory stimuli will excite him beyond belief, and you will soon feel his tongue pushing aside your fingers as he eagerly seeks the flesh you have been touching. And you will also find that by letting him see the spots to which your own fingers stray, he becomes more adept at locating them with his tongue.

February 17

Try an experiment with bondage—many men are excited by this.

Ask him—after first making it clear that nothing painful will be involved—to let you tie him down and sexually torment him. After he agrees, as he probably will if you have made it clear that only harmless fun is to be involved, have him strip and lie down on the bed. Use nylons and other sheer materials to bind his wrists and ankles to the four corners of the bed. Leave him alone in the room.

Take your time about changing into something skimpy and exotic—boots and dark hose, for instance, and nothing else—as part of the pleasure of this sexual charade is derived from the mild agony caused by waiting for the unknown.

Return to the room with a sexy roll of your hips, letting his eyes take in your loveliness. Go to the bed and, using both your fingers and your lips, sexually caress his body. Take his penis into your mouth until it is fully hard. Then, without a word of warning, stand and leave the room.

Let him simmer for long moments.

When next you return to him let your caresses be of a diferent type. Lie atop him for a moment, letting him feel the warm softness of your breasts against his chest. Or straddle him so that he is looking directly up at the tempting flesh of your sex organs and is able, perhaps, to lift his head and kiss you there. Then once again leave the room.

Think of your own variations on these joyful forms of "torment" and continue them until the agony becomes unbearable.

Then untie him and be prepared to spend hours taking care of the need you have aroused in him.

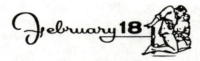

On a deck of cards write down a brief description of as many sexual positions and techniques as you can think of, one to each card. You need not have an item for each card in the deck.

Show him what you have done, let him add his own suggestions to the cards, and challenge him to a game of "War."

Shuffle the cards and each of you take half of the deck. Put your cards in a pile, facedown. Each player turns up a card, and the highest card captures the other. If there is a tie, the tied cards remain at stake and each player turns up another, with the winning card capturing all that are at stake. Play continues until one player has no cards remaining.

When only one sexual technique or position remains to be captured the game is over and the two of you bring to life that which is described on the card.

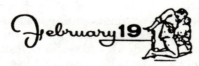

A good way to get him away from the television set. Let the commercials take the two of you through a striptease!

Instead of going to the kitchen for a snack or a bottle of beer when those boring messages flash on the screen, make an agreement that will turn the evening into one of pleasure; each time there is a commercial break, one of you removes an item of clothing from the other, taking turns.

The commercials on television are so plentiful that you will quickly reach a tempting state of semi-nudity and the television set will be completely forgotten.

February 20

Are you aware of those new, flavored douche powders? They come in a wide assortment of flavors, are available at most drug counters, and can be a delicious additive to oral sex.

Pick up a small assortment—strawberry, raspberry, and wild cherry for instance—and try one of them. Then entice him into a performance of cunnilingus and watch for the look of surprised pleasure that will spread across his face.

And watch his pleasure increase when you show him the assortment you have purchased and tell him you would like to know which is his favorite flavor. He will surely want to do a lot of tasting before he gives you an answer.

February 21

The rear-entry position is one that has been neglected by too many women, probably because of the many unsavory names that have been applied to it, yet it is a sexual position that can give great pleasure to both the male and the female.

Try kneeling on the bed, with your head bent low and resting on a pillow, while he bends over you. Let your pelvis begin to roll slowly as he enters you, and meet his thrusting penis with a rocking of your body. You will find that lowering your hips increases the friction between clitoris and penis, thus increasing both your pleasure and his. And this position easily allows you to reach back between your thighs to squeeze and fondle his testicles—to which he will respond by filling you with the full length of his erection.

February 22

See how a complete change of location can add spice to your loving!

Arrange for him to take you out tonight. Be dressed in your most sexy outfit, as if this were your first date. As the evening progresses, let your eyes and your hands convey to him the sexual excitement you feel. Dance with your body pressed close to his, your pelvis weaving against his. Be young and full of life.

Then, when the night is drawing to a close, instead of letting him take you home, insist that he take you to a motel. Let the room clerk believe you are a pair of young lovers engaged in an illicit meeting—and be just that when the door to the room has closed behind you.

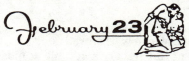

February 23

Too many women confuse fellatio with masturbation; they bestow oral caresses upon the penis of the man, but use the hand and fingers to bring him to climax.

Tonight, without using your hands at all, see if you can orally bring him to orgasm.

Only the most experienced in the art of fellatio can accomplish this. To do it, you will have to use every oral skill you possess.

Use your hands and fingers to tease his thighs and stomach, but keep them away from his penis and testicles. Let your flicking tongue bring him to full erection, and then take this softly between your lips. Raise and lower your head, letting your lips glide over his shaft, and let your tongue swirl over its tip.

Try holding the tip of it between your lips and letting your warm breath play over it; take as much of the shaft as you possibly can into your mouth, and then as your lips retreat, apply a strong suction. And don't forget to let him feel the touch of your lips on his testicles and the base of his penis.

Though you may not be able to bring about his orgasm in this manner—at least on your first attempt—you will probably come very close. And he will love you for the effort.

February 24

Here is a sex position the two of you will love!

You sit in an armchair, with him kneeling before you. Have your legs spread, your feet just past his knees, on the outside of them. This position, of course, literally begs him to perform cunnilingus on you, or to draw you down so that he may kiss your breasts.

Let him use any such foreplay he wishes. Then, when he is fully erect and ready, let yourself slide slowly down onto his lap, so that you are impaled upon his penis.

Your back will then be resting against the seat of the armchair, your legs around his body, and you will have the leverage with which to control the copulatory gyrations of your lower body. He will be helping you with his hands on your waist or buttocks, and your breasts will be convenient for his tasting. A fun position, all in all.

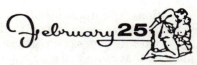

February 25

Satin sheets can be one of the most rewarding additions you will ever make to your bedroom decor. And they have become fairly inexpensive, so why not try them today?

Pick exotic colors that go well with the rest of your bedroom decor, and be especially careful to see that they enhance your bedroom wardrobe. These sheets are available in silver, scarlet, black, emerald, blue, and many, many other colors, and matching or contrasting pillow cases can usually be obtained.

But far more important than the color they add to your bedroom is the feeling of luxurious sleekness you will feel against your bodies as you make love on the bed covered by them. A touch of your own cologne will give them your own personal scent and make them doubly appealing to the man who shares your bed.

February 26

While people have spent centuries searching for a true aphrodisiac, the best one in existence is the human mind. See if this little trick doesn't arouse him.

Dim the lights and put on some soft music before he arrives, then brew a very strong pot of tea. Flavor it with sweet spices to disguise the taste.

When he arrives, tell him the potion is an aphrodisiac that was given to you by a friend, and that this friend has tried it and found it effective. Pour a cup for each of you.

Let a little time pass and have a second cup. Pretend that you feel slightly giddy, a little light-headed, but try not to overact. At the same time make your voice throaty, your movements sexy, and ask if he is feeling any effects.

If you have played upon his psyche properly, and if the setting and the mood is properly erotic, he *will* be aroused. He may or may not attribute this to the potion, but what is the difference? The end result is what counts.

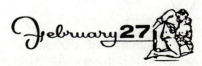

February 27

Start a diary today. In it describe, in great detail, your favorite sexual techniques and positions. Use his name often, and refer to the certain most exciting things he has done to you in the recent past.

Then leave the diary, with its pages open, where he will be certain to find it. Leave him alone in that room and give him time to look through it. Don't mention the book at all.

He will soon be performing those most exciting acts again.

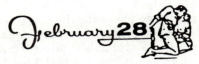

Tonight give him the exquisite pleasure of a sexual position in which you do all the "work."

Have him lie on his back while you move into a sitting position over his penis. Draw your legs up in front of you, rest your hands on his chest for support, then raise and lower your body to move his penis in and out, in and out.

This position affords him the luxury of watching your body as it moves above him, leaves his hands free to stroke your naked breasts, buttocks, and pubis; and you will soon feel his hips rising to drive his penis deep in response to each lowering of your body.

Leap Year! The day when a woman may break tradition and propose to a man. Take advantage of it.

Call his attention to this date, remind him of the tradition behind it, and get him to agree to accept all your proposals for the evening; making him, in effect, your slave for the day.

Then propose only things that will be even more pleasing to him than to you.

On this date in 1933, a man named Alfred Mosher Butts invented an adult word game that became famous and swept the country under the name Scrabble.

Celebrate this event by challenging your man to a game of Scrabble, using only explicit sexual words. Follow the regular rules of the game, but ban any word not closely connected with sex.

When the game is over, let the winner collect a prize by taking all the words from the board and forming them, as nearly as possible, into a sentence. This sentence then becomes a sexual command the loser must obey. A great game for cold, windy nights.

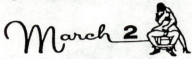

March 2

Arrange for an evening out. Dress very sexily, but be very cool and demure as you leave the house. Then when you are in the car and it is too late for him to do anything about it, lean over, kiss him—and guide his hand beneath your skirt to reveal that you are wearing no panties!

Don't let him talk you into returning home; make him go through with the plans for the evening, whatever they may be.

To most men this bit of daring can be very exciting, and as the evening wears on, he will be unable to push from his mind the vision of the nakedness that lies beneath your skirt. If the two of you are dancing this night, his arousal will be even greater, and you may have to make a short night of it to keep him from exploding.

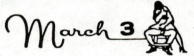

March 3

Better have old sheets on the bed tonight!

Take a jar of strawberry jam to bed with you. Spread it over his nipples, his penis, his testicles, in the cleft between his buttocks—then slowly, sensually lick it off his body. Then let him take his turn.

You will find that he is more than eager to cleanse the thick, sweet jam from your breasts, vaginal lips, and perhaps, even from your anus. And by the time the two of you have completed the sweet task of cleansing one another's bodies, you will be so excited by the licking, stroking tongues upon your flesh that the sex that follows may take any one of many delicious twists and turns. And the shower that follows is likely to cause the whole evening to start anew.

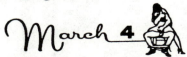

March 4

Try this technique to add a new thrill to the old male-dominant sexual position.

36

As he moves above you, draw your knees up until your thighs are touching your breasts. Lock your lower legs behind his back and squeeze with all your strength. Then slowly lower one leg, letting the soft flesh of your inner thigh caress him, until it lies straight.

Once again draw your leg up, bending the lower part around him, and squeeze. Then repeat this motion with the other leg, as his penis slips in and out of you.

Nylons can make your shifting legs feel even better against his naked skin; and by raking his buttocks excitedly with your nails, but not, of course, inflicting real pain, you can make the male-dominant position one of the most exciting of all.

March 5

Do you know why, when you fellate him, he often asks you to swallow his semen? Or why pictures of smiling girls with semen-spattered faces and dripping lips are among the most popular in visual erotica? There are sound psychological reasons.

The male can derive no real physical pleasure from the ingestion of his semen, for it must come after the completion of the sexual act. But he derives a great psychological pleasure. By accepting his fluids you convey a sense that you have totally accepted him; and by rejecting it, if you do, you convey a vague feeling that you have rejected him.

Tonight—you are going to express your total acceptance of him!

Many women find the thought of swallowing the male seminal fluids repulsive; but here, too the reasons are largely psychological. Put aside your prejudices and try.

Use every oral technique you know to bring him close to climax, and then, when the thrashing of his body and the hot pulsing of his penis warn you he is about to erupt, force your lips far down over his shaft. Stay there as long as you can.

Though you may be slightly gagged by the hot, spewing fluid, you will find that it is very nearly tasteless and far less nauseating than you had expected. You may very well learn to love it, as many women do, and he will long remember and be aroused by the sight of you bending over his penis with wet, dripping lips.

March 6

Try this exercise in sensuality. Practice it often, put it to use when you are with him, and it can greatly increase your effectiveness as a lover.

1. Fully clothed, stand so that your pubic mound is pressed against some hard object such as a doorknob or the corner of a table. Put your hands on your hips and close your eyes.

2. Let your hips begin to move in a slow, sensual roll, moving your lower body against the object you are using. Try to imagine that object is *him*.

3. Continue the movements of your hips, varying them in as many sexual movements as you can, and slowly move your hands up to your breasts. Caress them until the nipples are throbbing.

4. Try your best to reach orgasm through this method, and though you may not be able to do so at first, you will soon find your hips creating alluring sexual patterns of movements that you thought were beyond your capabilities.

Try putting these newly-discovered movements to use while dancing with him, or embracing. A great invitation to love!

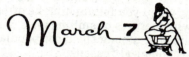

Be in the tub when he arrives, with thick, perfumed bubbles barely covering your body. Invite him into the bathroom, give him a soft sponge, and ask him to sit on the edge of the tub while he uses it.

You will soon find that his hands wander repeatedly to your breasts, stomach, and pubis, and that he is more than ready to share your tub with you. Surprise him by refusing. And give him an even greater treat.

While his hands and eyes wander over your naked body, let your own fingers move to his fly and free his erect penis. Take it into your mouth and tease it until he is brought to climax—which will be very soon because of the natural erotic appeal of the situation.

Then leave the tub, hand him a towel, and ask him to dry you off. Let your body writhe sensually before his eyes as he does so, let your excited fingers return time after time to his penis, and you will soon find his sexual stamina restored.

Then let him put this stamina to use.

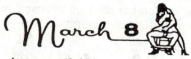

Be his topless waitress tonight!

Have his favorite food and drink prepared before he arrives, the lights dimmed, the table set, music playing. Be fully dressed when he arrives to take all this in, then excuse yourself and remove your blouse and bra. Return to the room and tell him that the rules are "look, but

38

don't touch," just as they would be in any topless nitery.

Enforce your rule, but let your naked breasts brush enticingly against him as you coyly serve the food and drink you have prepared.

You will soon find yourself not only topless and bottomless, but in the bedroom watching him shed his own clothes.

Buy a package of Chinese fortune cookies. Open one of the cookies and insert a note telling him what you are going to do to him at the first opportunity. Reseal the cookie.

Get him to take you to dinner at a Chinese restaurant, and be sure he orders a meal that includes these cookies. Then switch your cookies for the one brought by the waiter.

He may be somewhat startled when he reads your message, but he will soon recover enough to help you into your coat and rush you home to bed, where he will hold you to your promise.

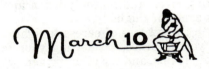

Be dressed in a sheer blouse and short, short skirt when you greet him, and be naked under these. As you embrace, lead him into a position that places your back against a wall.

With your breasts pressed against his chest and your tongue snaking hotly into his mouth, slip your arms around his neck. Then slowly lift one leg and bend your knee so your lower leg goes behind his thighs, very high up.

This will, of course, cause your brief skirt to slip up onto your thighs, and soon you will feel his hand moving between your legs to discover your nudity. Then is the time to let your own hand go to work on his zipper.

This brings you into a standing position for sexual intercourse that is especially exciting because of its apparent spontaneity, and you will find that leaning back on your shoulders allows you to roll your hips with great freedom, almost as if they were mounted on well-lubricated ball bearings. His hands under your buttocks will, of course, assist your movements.

March 11

Arrange a mirror so that he will be able to watch your writhing images as the two of you make love. Begin by undressing yourself tonight, instead of having him do it, and stand so that he can watch your reflection in the mirror. Turn the act of undressing into a seductive striptease.

When you are in his arms, without calling his attention to what you are doing, position yourself so that he will be able to look into the mirror and catch every detail of the action as your tongue caresses his body and his genitals, and so he will be able to see the parting of your flesh as, at long last, his penis enters you.

There is a little of the voyeur in every man, and with the simple placement of a mirror you can use that trait to increase his satisfaction. Why not give it a try tonight?

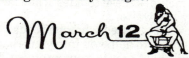

March 12

Biting, nipping, nibbling, licking, and sucking can add greatly to the pleasures of making love—and not only when applied to the better-known erogenous zones of the body.

Experiment with these types of caress tonight!

As the two of you embrace, try letting your tongue move wetly around the edge of his lips, and try nibbling gently at them with your teeth. Nip the lobe of his ear, his neck, and his chest. Let the tip of your tongue lash out to wet his face.

Here is an especially effective way these techniques may be applied while making love. Have him enter you from behind, while the two of you lie on your sides. As he reaches around to cover your breasts, take his hands into yours and draw them up to your lips. Let your tongue caress the palms of his hands. Take his fingers, one at a time, into your mouth and suck them. As his excitement increases and you feel the faster plunging of his penis, try biting down on his fingers, applying a gentle but steadily increasing pressure. And don't be surprised when, in his growing rapture, he draws your hands back over your shoulders to return caresses of the same nature.

March 13

Call him at work. Ask him to stop at an adult bookstore and buy you an erotic book. Tell him to make the selection. The type of erotica he chooses will be a good indication of his own interests.

When he brings it to you, snuggle up to him and have him read passages from the book to you; or, if it is strictly visual erotica, look at the photographs with him. Let your fingers make an occasional check of his arousal.

Very soon the book will be cast aside and the two of you will be creating your own erotica.

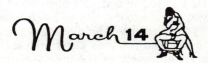

Cunnilingus, as a part of foreplay, can be just as exciting and rewarding to him as it is to you; yet many women, while they quite often try varied positions for sexual intercourse, seldom use more than one position for this act of oralism.

Try this variation tonight.

Beneath a sheer and revealing gown, be naked or wear only a pair of crotchless panties. Let the gown be transparent enough to reveal a shadowy hint of the triangle of hair surrounding your vulva, as this faint outline can sometimes be far more exciting to a man than total nudity.

When he takes you in his arms to kiss you, as he certainly will, be standing beside a sofa, chair, or the bed. Use excited, fluttering fingers and other body language to indicate to him how anxious you are to feel his lips and tongue between your thighs. Let the gown part as his kisses move down your body.

As he kneels and nears his goal, lift one leg and place that foot on the sofa or bed beside which you are standing. Slide your other foot out until you are spread wide for his kisses, and use your trembling hands on his shoulders and neck for support. Let your hips swing and swivel before him.

His hands under your buttocks will be helping to support you as he attacks this delicious task with new eagerness. He may lift your thigh even higer to drape it over his shoulder, and soon the two os you will discover the hidden advantage of engaging in cunnilingus while you are standing beside the bed or sofa.

When the sweet agony of his kisses grows intolerable, you can collapse onto your back and seek relief in any way you wish.

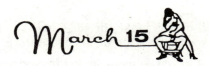

March 15

Try this mild experiment with bondage. You may find it to your liking, and it is certain that he will love it, as it encourages him to act out wishes he may be too inhibited to otherwise attempt.

Lay down the ground rules before you start. Make it clear there is to be no real pain involved. Let him be aware of any acts that are to be off limits. Set a time limit, if you wish.

Then have him tie you to the bed, in a position of his own choosing, and tell him that you are his to do with as he chooses. You are almost certain to find that your position of helplessness encourages him to try things that surprise you, and you may also find it thrilling to be in a position where you are completely at the mercy of the man you love.

This is a quite harmless way of exploring the sado-masochistic streak that lies hidden in all humans, and the fun it provides, if kept carefully under control, makes it well worth the effort.

March 16

Here is a trick that was known to the courtesans of days gone by, and one you can use to drive him to new heights of ecstasy.

Let him know you have a surprise in store for him, since you are going to need his cooperation. Have him lie on his back, naked, while with your fingers and lips you bring him to full erection.

When his penis is hard and throbbing, take a silk handkerchief, twisted into a cord, and wrap it twice around his shaft, about halfway up. Arrange the cord so you can pull on the ends to tighten it. Draw on the ends until he gives the first indication that it is becoming painful, then ease up a bit.

Now fellate him, using every trick you know, until the taut quivering of his body tells you he is about to reach his climax—then quickly tighten the cord around his penis. This will delay his eruption.

Ease up on the cord and begin anew. Draw the silken cord tight each time he approaches climax, but continue your oral caresses while it holds back his ejaculation. His orgasm can be delayed almost indefinitely in this manner, but when you remove that silken cord for the final time—watch out!

His climax will be spectacular!

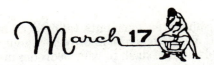

March 17

Do you remember when it was traditional for a girl to give her lover a lock of her hair as a memento to remember her by? Why not continue this tradition, but with a unique, loving twist all your own?

Snip off a lock of your pubic hair. Tie one end tightly with bright thread. Place the curl in one of those plastic windows that he can insert in the picture section of his billfold, after first adding a bit of your own perfume. This will keep you in his thoughts when he is away, and it takes little imagination to see the direction those thoughts will take each time he looks at this gift.

March 18

Simultaneous fellatio and cunnilingus, commonly known as "69," offers so much pleasure to the male because it plays upon all his senses; while seeing and tasting your delicate flesh and feeling it also, he both hears your own sighs of pleasure and experiences the feel of your lips and tongue against his penis.

Why not surprise him with this delightful act tonight?

Guide him into this rewarding and classic position by letting your lips cover his naked body with kisses, moving always closer to his erected penis, and turning your own body as you do so.

By the time your lips engulf his stiffness and you lift one leg to straddle him, he will need no further indication of your intent. You will feel his head rising between your thighs to taste you, and the oral manipulations you are using on his penis will be doubly pleasurable because of the stimuli he is receiving as he licks and kisses your wet and quivering vulva.

March 19

You are very careful, of course, about your own bedroom wardrobe, but have you thought of adding to his? Many specialty shops now offer a wide array of extremely erotic undergarments for the male, as well as for the female. If there is no such shop in your town, the same items can be purchased from mail-order firms that advertise in the male-interest magazines.

You will be able to select from such items as bikini-like shorts, or transparent ones, and even garments tailored from white or black leather. Such a gift clearly lets him know where your thoughts lie, and you will find it adds a bit of dash to your bedroom moments together.

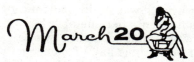

The secret to the enjoyment of anal intercourse, for the female, lies in learning to relax the muscles of the sphincter, thus easing the entry of the penis. This exercise will help you overcome the tendency to tauten muscles. Try it today and practice it often.

   1. Use Vaseline, K-Y jelly, or any other suitable lubricant to make penetration easier. As you apply the lubricant to the anus, let your fingers move in a stimulating manner. Lie down on the bed, nude and resting on your side, and create erotic images in your mind.
   2. Use a battery-operated, torpedo-shaped vibrator (they can be purchased at most drug counters, and are invaluable) to further stimulate your anal senses.
   3. Begin by placing the tip of it lightly against the entry to the anus, letting those vibrations bring your nerves to life, and then turning it off and on. Turn it off and insert only the tip into the anus, and turn it on once again. As you begin to feel the pleasure caused by the vibrating instrument (and you will!) use your fingers on your clitoris until you reach climax.

You will find, after you have tried this a few times, that you are thrusting the vibrator deeper and deeper into your anus and that the climaxes caused by your stroking fingers are coming faster and more often.
   And that is when you will truly be able to enjoy anal intercourse with *him!*

Many men are intrigued by the sight of a shaved pubes, you know, so you must want to see how he feels about this. Discuss it with him tonight.
   Keeping in mind that this shaved state can be difficult to maintain, and that the regrowing hair can be a prickly nuisance until they be-

come long enough to regain their softness, let him know you are willing to do this to please him.

Then have him help you shave it.

You might want to compromise on this by shaving the pubic hair down until only an enticing bit of fluff remains around the pink lips of the vagina. He will gladly let you know which he prefers.

You know that a change of position or a change of location gives added pleasure to your lovemaking, but have you tried to vary the time? Most couples fall into a pattern of making love at about the same time of day.

Break this habit tonight!

Set the alarm clock for the wee hours of the morning. When it goes off, awaken him with your breasts against him, your fingers or your lips toying with his penis. He will quickly respond.

Sex can be at its best in the lazy hours of early morning, before the pressures of the daily rat race have taken their toll, and you will agree that this is a most enjoyable way to greet the day.

Use a Polaroid camera to take nude and seminude bedroom photos of *him*. Direct his poses, and use your fingers teasingly on his penis, so you can capture the image of his erection.

You will soon hear him asking you to pose, and the poses he asks you to take, the sexy garments he asks you to wear, will provide you with valuable clues about what really excites him.

Alcohol, contrary to the opinion held by many people, is a depressant and has a negative effect on the enjoyment of sex. But tonight you are going to explore one of the ways it can be used to make sex more enjoyable!

Take a bottle of champagne or another good wine to bed with you. Give him one glass to relax with; then, while he sips this, pour a few drops of the beverage on his body, scattering them from his chest to his testicles. Slowly lick these away.

Then offer him a drink from your body.

You will find that his thirst for the beverage grows greater as he laps it from your breasts, navel, and vagina; and don't be surprised or offended if he wants to insert the tip of the bottle into your body and fill you with fluid to be sucked out by his thirsting mouth. Though you may object to this last, the desire is common enough among men.

In any case, the two of you will quickly and happily consume the contents of that bottle while at the same time devouring one another.

Make a very, very erotic tape recording and address it to him. Describe in great detail an act of love that you would like to commit with him. Start the recorder as he arrives at the door, then conceal yourself in the bedroom closet. He will enter the room, listen in pleasant surprise to the recording, and come after you when he hears this final sentence, which you have tactfully added to your recording: "The speaker can be found hiding in the bedroom closet!"

Just to show your love for him, try serving him a meal in bed. It is a treat all men love, few receive, and one which can be so easily given.

The meal need not be elaborate; it is the thought that counts.

Make him comfortable, wear something sexy and revealing while serving it, and sit chatting with him while he eats.

You will likely discover that he wants you for dessert.

Invite him to take a bath with you. Be in the tub, on your back, totally nude, with the water turned on to the slightest trickle and slowly rising around you, when he arrives. He will take it from there.

Sex in the water can be incredibly enjoyable. As the water slowly rises to cover your nude, locked bodies, you will experience voluptuous sensations no other form of sex provides.

Just keep one eye on the level of the water!

March 28

Give him the unexpected thrill of anal intercourse!

Before he arrives lubricate your anal entry with Vaseline, baby oil, or K-Y jelly. Say nothing to him about it. But quickly let him know you are eager for sex.

Guide him into any position he normally uses when entering your vagina from the rear. But as he places the tip of his penis to the lips of your vagina, reach down, without a word, and raise it to your anus.

He will be caught by surprise, but as he feels the slippery welcome you have prepared for him, without any coaxing, he will slowly ease his hardness into the tight tunnel that awaits him. Let your muscles relax as you accept him, direct your hands and his to your *mons* and other erogenous zones, and the two of you will be well on your way to a mutually enjoyable sexual experience.

March 29

Ask him to take a nap with you.

Later, when he is dozing, and making every effort not to waken him, unzip his trousers and free his penis. Watch his face as you tease it lightly with the tips of your fingers. Touch it with the tip of your tongue, take it between your lips and suck it gently, and lap it until he is in full erection.

A sleeping man is especially sensitive to sexual stimulation and when he awakens, as he soon will, no matter how great your care, he will be tremendously aroused by the scene which greets him. To see that a woman craves him so greatly is one of the most satisfying things a man can experience.

March 30

Masturbation was the first form of sex experienced by almost every man who ever lived, and by nearly every woman. Almost every man recalls, from the years of his youth, a girl who, out of fear of pregnancy or for other reasons, would not engage in intercourse but would quite willingly engage in masturbation. The hands of a knowing female can be a potent sexual weapon, so why should you not use yours on him?

Put those hands to work tonight!

One of the most exciting ways to do this is to casually lead your talk around to a discussion of such childhood practices and coax him into admitting such experiences of his own with girls. You can encourage such admissions by giving real or imagined details of your own similar adventures. When this talk has progressed to the proper point, coyly suggest that it might be fun to relive such moments; he will quickly agree.

Although you might want to give him this pleasure while locked in tight embrace, your tongues meeting and his hand at work on your clitoris, he might be even more thrilled by the following variation.

Lie naked behind him, your breasts flattened against his back, your pubic triangle teasing his buttocks, your lips and tongue at work on his neck and shoulders, and slip both arms around his body to grasp his penis and testicles.

Let your naked body writhe against him as with the fingers of one hand you manipulate the hairy flesh of his testicles, and with the other you masturbate his hardened shaft. Soon you will feel his hot fluids spilling over your hands, but with only a few more strokes of your teasing fingers, a few gyrations of your nude body, you will have him between your thighs, ready to go again.

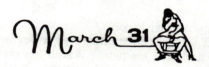

The last day of the first quarter of the year. A good time to look at your relationship with him and look for ways in which it can be improved. Write the answers to the following questions on paper, being as truthful as you can. Your answers may surprise you.

1. Have you really tried to make each day a unique experience in living and loving?

2. How many sexual positions have you tried during this period?

3. How many times have you refused or avoided sex, even though you knew he really wanted it?

4. How many new erotic techniques have you tried during this period?

5. How many times have you refused to take part in a sexual experience that he wanted to try?

Keep this list hidden away and make a new one about once every third month, seeking always to improve on the answers.

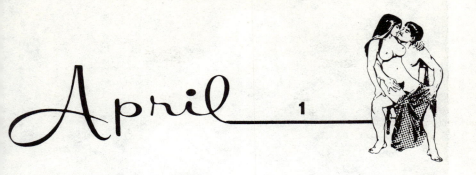

April 1

April Fools' Day!

Have a bag packed and tell him you are leaving. Ask him to drive you to the airport or bus terminal. Go through with this farce until you arrive there. Then inform him of the date, open the bag to reveal a few of your things plus his shaving gear, and have him take you to the motel where you have already made an overnight reservation.

April 2

Try this variation of the rear-entry position for a little added fun.

Standing, with your feet far apart, lean forward and support yourself by resting your hands on some low object such as a coffee table or the edge of a sofa. Slide your feet far back, so that your body is very near the horizontal. But be careful, don't fall.

This limits the rocking, or to-and-fro, motions of your body, but allows terrific freedom of movement for those sensuous rollings he loves to feel. As he stands between your legs, his hands on your hips or beneath your stomach, he will raise your vagina to the level that allows maximum penetration, and your slow, weaving undulations will assure that it also offers maximum pleasure—to both of you.

April 3

We are well into the first days of spring now, the season which, according to tradition, arrives along with the first bluebird.

Use food coloring and your reflection in the mirror to paint a

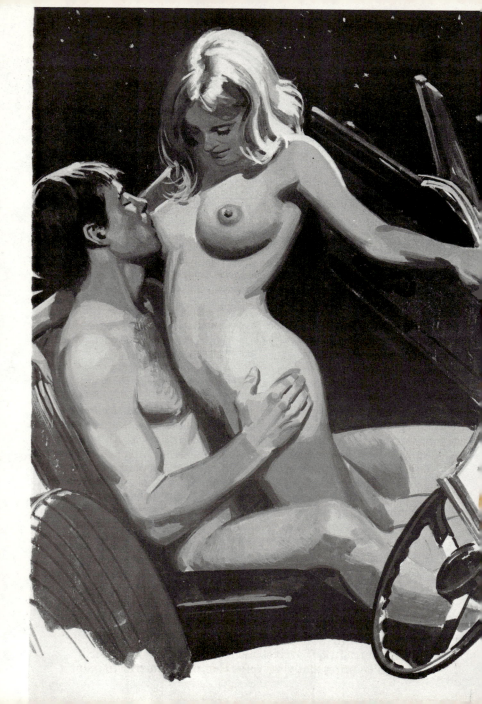

bluebird on your lower stomach, just above your pubis. Then dress skimpily and sexily, and wait for him to arrive.

Tell him there is a sign of spring hidden in your apartment, and give him twenty questions in which to identify and locate it. Even with the helpful answers you give, he may not be able to do so, but when at last you disclose the item for which he has been searching, this will make little difference.

He will quite gladly help you remove the bluebird.

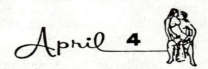

April 4

Try this way of renewing his sexual vigors for a second round of love. As he approaches his first climax, roll over on top of him and continue until you feel the warmth of his ejaculation. Now move into a kneeling position, being careful to keep his penis in the warm, damp grasp of your vagina, and lower yourself so that your buttocks are against his groin.

Draw his hands up to your lips and caress them for a moment, then ease them down to your breasts. When his hands close tightly over your breasts, let your own fingers move down to the base of his penis. Lift yourself until only the tip of his penis remains in your vagina, guiding it, if needed, with your fingers.

Use your fingers to gently manipulate the outer skin of his penis over its core, masturbating him, in effect, while still holding its tip in your vagina. With your other hand caress his belly, chest, and outer thighs.

Very soon, you will begin to feel the return of his hardness, his hands will leave your breasts to slip around your body and draw you closer, and the two of you will be enjoying the results of your efforts.

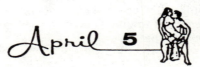

April 5

Challenge him to a bout of sensory perception.

Have him lie naked on the bed, with his eyes tightly closed, and tell him that you are going to touch his body with ten items of different types. Defy him to identify all ten.

Move about the room gathering the items you are going to use, and try to make as many of them as possible items that will appeal to his erotic senses: panties, a feather, lace, etc.

Now remove your bra.

Very, very lightly touch his thigh or chest with one item after another. Then, as the tenth test of his senses, let your nipple touch his body briefly and lightly, always being sure his eyes remain closed.

After a few attempts he will begin to identify the other items, and, if you are touching them to his body in a teasing, caressing manner, he will be growing excited. But the slight deception of removing your bra after the game began should cause identification of that tenth item to elude him.

And when he opens his eyes to discover your deception he will begin to so thoroughly familiarize himself with that item that its feel —and its taste—will never mislead him again.

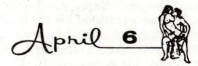

April 6

Try this position for fellating him.

Lie on your back, with your head just over the edge of the bed, so you are able to lower it fully. Have him stand with one leg on each side of your head, his penis directly over your face, and lean forward so that his hands are beside your hips and his face over your stomach.

Throw your head far back as you take him into your mouth and begin to fellate him, and you will find that this position has caused the muscles of your upper throat to relax, thus allowing him deeper penetration than you had thought possible. You will also find that this position offers two other pleasurable benefits; not only can he lower his hips to thrust his penis into your mouth, just as he would thrust it into your vagina, but your parted thighs, directly under his face, openly invite him to lean down and use his tongue and lips to give you your own satisfaction.

You can safely bet that he will!

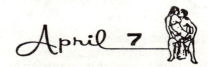

April 7

You know that no woman likes a man who rolls over onto his back and goes to sleep the moment he is finished making love, but are you also aware that the reverse is equally true? Too many women are not.

The moments following love are the best time to express your affection. This is the one time you should cling to a man, showing him how reluctant you are to have him withdraw. Let your lips cover his face with soft, tender kisses in the instant before he does, and continue to stroke his body with loving fingers. And don't forget to let those fingers clutch his softening penis.

The moment after sex should not be the moment when love ends; in many cases, it is the moment when true love starts. And why not try what many men consider the ultimate show of affection? Bend down to bestow a few soft and loving kisses on the penis that is the source of so much joy for each of you, as the final caress of the night.

Start tonight to pay more attention to his needs in the moments following sex, adding whispered phrases of love to your physical gestures, and you will find that not only will your sex become more frequent, it will become more enjoyable.

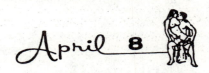

April 8

Wigs are now inexpensive enough to be within the reach of every woman, and they can also add a real flair to your sex life. Indulge in this little expenditure today, and enjoy the results.

Don't be wearing your new hair when he arrives. Let him make himself comfortable in the bedroom or in his favorite chair, and then give him his surprise.

Appear before him wearing a nightie that clearly reveals each line of your lovely body, or your sexiest bra and panties, or a dress that begs to be removed—and hair of a completely different length or color or style from that to which he has grown accustomed.

Suggesting as it does a totally different female, this sudden change is one which most men find especially provocative. You will almost certainly see a new gleam in his eyes as he takes you into his arms and begins making love to the new you, and there will be many nights in the future when he will ask you to don that wig.

Here is an added tip you might want to consider when choosing a wig; many men are especially excited by women whose tresses are a color that contrasts to that of their pubic hair.

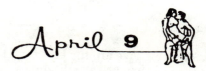

April 9

Challenge him to a game of "Stop."

The idea is to prolong, for as long as is possible, both the foreplay and the act of sex which follows. Begin by taking turns removing each other's clothing—one item of yours followed by one item of his—until the two of you are nude, and then take turns bestowing arousing kisses upon the bodies of one another. Let the action become progressively more sexual, and let anything that is mutually agreeable be acceptable. Either partner may bring the action to a temporary halt by crying "Stop!" and it then becomes his or her turn to proceed.

The first to ignore the call for a "Stop," even if it comes in the middle of copulatory movement, is the loser and must pay the penalty upon which you have previously agreed.

Intercourse may be prolonged to a tremendous length by this playful little technique, and it can be made so enjoyable that neither of you will want to stop.

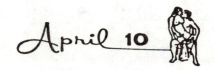

April 10

Do you know what is meant by the slang term "around the world"? Described in similar slang, it is "straight," "French," and "Greek" sex all rolled into one bundle of pleasure; or, more properly described, it is a sensuous combination of vaginal, oral, and anal sex.

Take him on a trip around the world tonight!

Wear a pair of crotchless panties, and add to his arousal by letting him know your intent. Begin by having him lie on his back while you fellate him, and be sure to turn so that your vagina is offered to his mouth. As you expertly tease his penis with lips and tongue, try slipping one hand under and between his buttocks to give him the additional thrill of anal stimulation.

Next lead him into vaginal copulation, with you selecting the position and guiding him to it. Part of his excitement will be due to the way you are taking the lead, and this added bit of aggressiveness will stimulate him further.

Then, just as he is about to climax—or after he has done so, and you have used oral and manual manipulation to restore his erection—have him resume the position on his back while you station yourself above him, facing toward his feet, kneeling so that your anus is poised above the tip of his erection. Let him hold your buttocks apart as you lower yourself onto it. When he has entered you, rock slowly back and forth above him, allowing him deeper penetration with each backward roll of your hips, and use your hands to tease his testicles as you do.

You will find that he can quite easily be brought to orgasm by each part of this technique, and you may wish to prolong each part to that extent. You may also wish to vary the order of the three parts of the act, which is fine. One word of caution is in order: Anal intercourse should never be followed by vaginal intercourse without first carefully washing the penis; a failure to do so may possibly lead to vaginal infection.

Happy traveling!

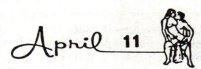

April 11

Give him an unusual bit of visual stimulation tonight.

Almost all large department stores now have a department which sells psychedelic lighting and wall posters; and there, usually at a cost of less than two dollars, you can purchase a light bulb that casts the same "black" light used in many nightclubs. Buy one, and you will find it a worthwhile expenditure.

White glows with uncanny brilliance beneath this light; your panties and bra will shimmer with new hues, your nipples will seem to glow as he kisses them, and your bedroom will become as erotic as that of any harem. The effect created by this sudden change in the lighting of your bedroom can be a powerful stimulant to his amorous intent, so give it a try tonight.

And watch his voltage go up.

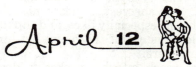

April 12

Using throw pillows and thick, soft blankets, prepare a comfortable sitting place on the floor. Put it before the fireplace, if you have one. Dress in a very short skirt, sheer blouse, and sexy underthings, then wait for his arrival.

Serve dinner to him on the place you have prepared, sitting

down on the floor to eat, as they do in many Eastern countries. Any position you take as you sit to eat will cause that short, short skirt to move revealingly up onto your thighs, and soon he will be pushing those dinner plates aside as he reaches for you.

That is why you wanted those blankets to be soft and comfortable.

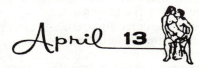

April 13

Let the two of you become characters in an erotic story!

Pick a good book that contains a highly erotic and totally descriptive sex scene between a male and a female character. Let it be the type of scene in which you really would like to participate.

Go through the pages with a pen and insert his name in place of the male character, your name in place of the female. Change the descriptions to match your own. This last will be easier than it sounds, as most writers do not give detailed physical descriptions, letting the imagination of the reader provide most of these.

Make him comfortable and tell him you want to read him a bedtime story. Let your voice be low and sultry, trembling with sexual excitement, as you do so. As he begins to realize what you have done, and your words create those erotic images in his mind, he will become more than eager to duplicate on the bed the scene you have created on paper.

After all, you told him it was going to be a bedtime story!

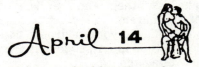

April 14

Try this little trick to make him remember you!

Select one of your sheerest, sexiest, most seductive pair of panties, a pair that he especially likes, and slip them in the pocket of his coat while he is out of the room. Let him leave without knowing they are there.

When he does reach into his pocket to discover that tiny, scented bit of silk, and it may be a matter of days before he does, his mind will be filled with a picture of you as he last saw you in them.

And he will hurry over to exchange them for the ones you have on. You can safely bet on that!

April 15

Wear a short skirt, with no panties under it, and draw him into a warm embrace as he enters the room. Cling to him with your arms around his neck, and slowly lift one leg to let him discover your bare bottom. As his hands slip under your buttocks, free his penis from his trousers and guide it to you, standing on one leg with the other curling around him.

His hands will tighten under your buttocks. As they do, lift your other leg and wrap it around him, so he is fully supporting your weight. You have quite literally placed yourself in his hands, and he will take it from there.

This is a terrific position, and by leading him to it the moment he enters, while he is still fully clothed, you convey a sense of hurried excitement that can be sexually intoxicating to him. And the depth of his thrusts will be just as intoxicating to you. Give it a try, and see.

April 16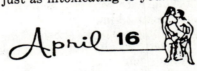

You are familiar, of course, with the extreme cold caused by deodorants and other aerosol sprays. Use that cold to give him a real sexual treat. But do it with a can of whipped cream or other food item, as the other sprays can be toxic.

Take the can to bed with you. Teasingly cover his penis with the whipped cream, then quickly take his penis fully into your mouth and let your lips slowly withdraw, taking with them the last traces of the sweet cream that covers him. Repeat this again and again, letting him feel the alternating sensations of the deep cold caused by the aerosol and the clinging warmth of your lips, and then fellate him to climax.

And don't be surprised if he wants to use the same technique on *you!*

April 17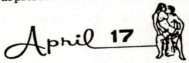

Give the two of you an extra thrill by bringing yourself to orgasm *before* he enters you. Then let him feel you quivering in orgasm after orgasm as his penis moves in and out, in and out, of your hot, wet vagina.

Wear crotchless panties, or no panties at all, and press your soft pubic mound tight against his thigh as you embrace. Let it writhe and weave against him, keeping pressure against your clitoris, and teasingly evade his attempts at starting intercourse. He loves the feel of your pubic hair and your flesh against him, and as that flesh grows hot and moist he will love it even more. Press yourself against all parts of his body—his chest, side, even his face—and use all your willpower to delay his entry until you have reached your first climax, or at least until your excitement is such that you can bear no more.

When at last you do take him between your thigs, you will be one quivering bundle of sexual energy, shaking violently with repeated orgasms, from the first thrust of his penis onward. And this is one time he will thank you for making him wait.

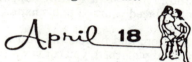

April **18**

This is the month of the famous "April showers," so don't let it go by without having him take one with you. Try luring him into the shower tonight without actually asking him.

Do this by repeatedly calling him to the shower to bring you the soap, shampoo, etc. Each time let him glimpse your naked body, and you might even ask him to soap your back.

When at last you have lured him into the shower—and that will not take very long—drop the soap and press your buttocks into his groin as you bend to retrieve it.

You will find that it is a long, pleasurable time before he allows you to straighten up.

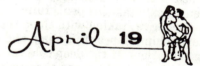

April **19**

It takes little imagination to understand the popularity of those topless shoeshine parlors that are popping up in so many of our major cities; it is the toplessness rather than the need of a shoeshine that lures men in.

Tonight give him a shoeshine.

Wear no bra, and a very sheer blouse, one that allows him to see the full outline of your breasts, the dark points of your nipples.

As you kneel before him vigorously using a brush and cloth to put a gleam on his shoes, the enticing sway of your breasts will also be putting a gleam in his eye. You will soon find yourself topless.

But a shoeshine will be the last thing on his mind.

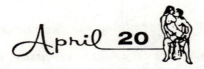

April 20

Here is a fabulous position, so why not give it a try tonight?

Have him lie on his back, naked, while you move over him, facing his feet, just as if you were going to sit on his lap—which you are, but with his penis inside you.

After you have assumed this position, and the full length of his penis is in you, slowly lean back until you are lying full-length atop his body.

You will find that your backward movement causes his penis to withdraw somewhat, and you may have to use your fingers to hold it in, but that can be an extra source of pleasure. Let your fingers rove over the part of the shaft that is drawn out by this movement, over his testicles, and encourage him to use his hand to manipulate the soft mound of flesh above your vagina. By resuming the sitting position, you can cause his penis to once again slip deep, and you will soon find him helping you to rock back and forth in this manner.

Movement is somewhat restricted in this position, which causes the two of you to use the hands somewhat more than usual, but it is an excellent one for prolonged intercourse.

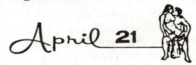

April 21

Do you remember the first time a boy took you for a ride in his car and, without a word, drove into a deserted, wooded lane and parked? And do you recall the thrill you felt as he took you in his arms to kiss you? Recreate that moment tonight—in reverse!

Ask him to go for a ride in the moonlight. You drive, and wear a skirt that will slip high on your thighs as you sit behind the wheel. Keep an idle conversation going as you drive, and try to divert his attention from where you are going. Take him to the most deserted spot you know, smile, turn off the headlights and the ignition, and let him take it from there. And if he hesitates, tell him you think you may be out of gas!

April 22

Try this visual stimulation tonight.

Arrange three large mirrors on opposite walls of your bedroom, so they will capture multiple reflections of what takes place on your bed.

Wear your briefest, most tempting undergarments, and strike a sexy pose for him.

As your image is repeatedly bounced from one mirror to another, surrounding him with your loveliness, you will soon hear him asking you to take one erotic position after another. That is the time to ask him to join you—and soon those mirrors will be filled with endless images of your locked, writhing bodies.

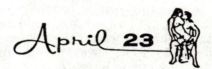

April 23

Play the hat game tonight—a game that, for very good reason, is extremely popular among the swinging set.

Each of you make a long list of sexual acts, ranging from the mildest kiss to the ultimate acts of intimacy, and give each act a number. Tear a sheet of paper into small strips, and on each strip write a number. Place these in a receptacle of any sort.

Take turns drawing numbers, with the person who draws the number committing the corresponding act. Let a few minutes lapse between each drawing, until you can't hold off anymore.

You will find that this is not only a good way for the two of you to shed away inhibitions you may have, but that it is an excellent way of probing the hidden sexual desires of your man, as he will often put down on paper the wants he might never express aloud.

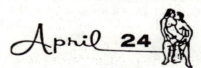

April 24

Try this technique of fellatio tonight. It is one of the best, and he is going to love it!

Draw your lips down over your teeth, so they form a soft oval and close this oval around his erected penis. Lower your head to take as much of him as possible into your mouth—then apply the strongest possible suction as you slowly draw your lips back up the length of his penis. When only the tip remains between your lips, relax the suction, then *quickly* lower your head to recapture the full length of his shaft.

Repeated over and over, these motions will quickly bring him to climax; and, unlike other oral techniques, this one usually works best when it is *not* varied.

Perhaps that is because no other way feels quite so good to the man!

60

April 25

Leave one of those torpedo-shaped personal vibrators where he can find it. Don't be ashamed to admit that it is yours, and don't be ashamed to admit that you use it. Most women do, and men know it.

Then don't be surprised or offended if he wants to watch you use it—most men are excited by the sight of female masturbation—or if he wants to use it on you. The two of you can learn a lot about your sexuality through such candor and such exploration.

And you will have double the fun because both the vibrator and his penis will be there for your enjoyment.

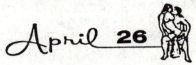

April 26

Try this little technique to add spice to your kisses. It is one used by women in many Latin American countries, and is both highly suggestive and arousing.

Wear a silk scarf around your neck, one that is lightly scented with cologne or perfume. When you meet him at the door and he takes you in his arms, stare directly into his eyes and take the corner of the scarf between your lips. Then kiss him.

As your lips meet, use the tip of your tongue to thrust the silk scarf into *his mouth,* then suck it gently into your own. Thrust it once again into his mouth. He will soon get the idea and his tongue will be lashing out to help.

This may sound farfetched, but try it and you will find that the feel of the silk between your two seeking tongues adds a new and exciting feel to your kisses—a feel that will soon guide his lips to other parts of your body.

April 27

Surprise him tonight with this little bit of anal stimulation!

Let your lips work their way down the length of his naked body and then turn to throw one leg over him, as if you were encouraging him to perform simultaneous fellatio and cunnilingus in the classic "69" position. Then go a little bit farther.

You will now be above him, your thighs straddling his face, and you will certainly feel his hands on your buttocks, his breath on your vagina. Lean far down between his legs and move your lips teasingly over his testicles—then down into the cleft between his buttocks. Grip his hard penis and move the outer skin back and forth as with the tip of your tongue you seek his anus, and you may soon feel his tongue leaving your vagina to seek *your* anal entry.

This is the time to put aside your prejudices and, as previously explained, remember that the human anus is as clean as most other parts of the body. The excitement such oral-anal contact adds to your sex life is well worth the trying—so try it tonight.

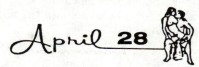

Put several records on the stereo, and have them set so they change automatically. Let the first records be slow, sensual music, and let the last ones have a faster beat. As the music begins to play, dim the lights and do a slow, suggestive striptease for him, in time to the music. And the records with a faster beat?

Let them set the pace for your lovemaking.

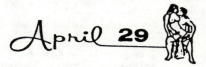

Take an old but attractive dress, one that fits rather loosely, and cut away the bottoms of the pockets. Be wearing the dress when he arrives, and pretend to be busy with your household chores. Needlessly fill both hands, then ask him to look in your pockets for some item that is just as needless as the ones you are holding. He will soon have both hands in your pockets up to his elbows, and you will have discovered that the old dress you are getting ready to remove has served its purpose.

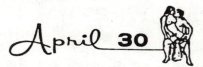

On this last day of the month give him something that will cause him to constantly remember you during the days ahead; let your lips cover the intimate parts of his body with those dull-red abrasions the teenagers refer to as "passion marks."

Do this by placing your parted lips against his skin, sucking hard, and then closing your teeth in light-but-steady pressure over the flesh that is drawn between them. Continue to suck hard while you are doing this.

The abrasions left on his skin by this type of caress cause a dull but pleasant ache that will linger for days, and that ache will be a constant reminder of you and how you left your mark, and he will soon come running back for more.

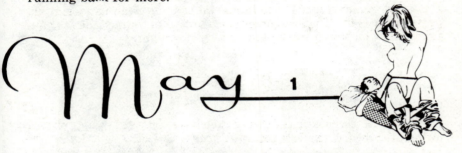

You know that every woman loves receiving flowers from a man, but have you ever considered buying them for him? They can be a powerful expression of love—especially when you add your own personal touch.

Buy a dozen long-stemmed roses. On the stem of each place a note beginning, "This is for the time. . . ." and giving a brief reminder of some intimate moment the two of you have shared. Return the flowers to their box and give them to him. He will discover the notes as he transfers the flowers to a vase.

And the two of you will soon have another moment well worth remembering.

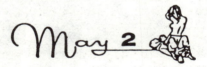

Add this exciting feature to your array of oral techniques tonight; it is one too often ignored.

Bend over his naked body as if you were going to perform fellatio, but let your lips move past the base of his penis, to his testicles. Let your tongue caress these for a moment, then part your lips and very gently, for they are sensitive, draw into your mouth one of the glands which lie within the sac.

Take these one after another into your mouth, letting him savor the warm wet feeling, and release them slowly through your lips. At the

same time, grip his hard penis in your fingers. Hold it lovingly against the side of your face. Let your fingers slowly slide the smooth outer skin up and down, and occasionally touch your tongue to its tip.

This offers him a truly arousing picture, and very soon his hands will encourage you to lift your head and take his penis fully into your mouth, or he will be moving between your thighs to give completion to what you have started.

Relax and enjoy the fruit of your efforts.

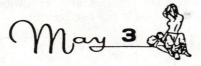

May 3

Here is a little secret that will make *his* oral efforts more enjoyable for both of you. And you may find that it encourages him to try it more often.

Wear the thinnest, most transparent pair of panties you own, a pair through which can clearly be seen the triangle of hair around your vulva, and even the pink folded flesh beneath. The panties should be small and bikini-like, allowing a few strands of pubic hair to curl from beneath the elastic.

With kisses and body language and excited, fluttering hands, make him aware that you want him to perform cunnilingus, and let him strip away everything but this skimpy, highly exciting bit of transparent silk or nylon. Stop him there, and use your hands to draw his face into the vee of your crotch exactly as you would do if you were naked.

He will soon get the idea, and you will feel his tongue begin to flicker across the scanty silk, tormenting the quivering flesh that lies beneath, and probing beneath the elastic to try and reach the tasty morsel the nylon covers.

The movement of his tongue and lips will cause the silk to move against your flesh in a stupendously exciting caress, soon bringing you to repeated orgasm, and your excitement will convey itself to him.

The pleasure he takes from cunnilingus is, after all, directly in proportion to the pleasure he gives you. Why not introduce him to this delicious method tonight?

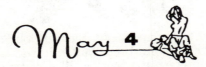

May 4

Here is an exercise in sensuality that will make you more skilled in the use of your tongue. Try it today and practice it often.

1. Lie on the bed with your eyes closed, the room dimly lit, soft music playing. Lift one hand to your lips and let your tongue move teasingly across the back of it, over the tip of each finger, and into the palm. Then slowly lick your way up the length of your arm, keeping your eyes closed and trying to imagine it is *his* tongue that is caressing you. Do the same with the other arm.

2. Draw your knees up, one at a time, and swirl the tip of your tongue over them. See how intense a reaction you can cause in your own body through this method, and try always to find new movements that will intensify the excitement.

Remember—a motion that is exciting to you will be twice as exciting to him.

Here is the ultimate way to explore his erogenous zones!

Have him lie naked on his back. Naked, or very nearly so, move over him and give him what has been commonly known as a "tongue bath." That's right. Use your tongue as if you were trying to cleanse his entire body. It will lead you to erogenous zones of which you were totally unaware.

Begin by letting your tongue flicker across his face; then cover his neck, chest, and stomach with wet caresses, and move from there to his feet. Many men are sexually excited by having a woman caress their feet, so take your time here. Let the tip of your tongue play slowly over the soles, then take his toes, one at a time, into your mouth and suck them, exactly as if you were fellating him. Every nerve in his body will be alive and quivering as you leave his feet and begin to lick his legs and inner thighs. By the time you have covered his testicles and the base of his penis, he will be so close to orgasm that you will have to hurriedly take him into your mouth to capture the reward for your efforts.

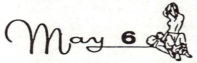

Buy an illustrated erotic magazine. Even if your community has banned the "hard-core" publications, you will find that most newsstands carry male-interest magazines filled with erotic pictures, though these do not actually show penetration.

Select the most exciting full-page illustration you can find and carefully tear this page from the magazine. Glue it to a heavy paper backing, being careful not to wrinkle it. Use a razor blade to cut it into small, irregular pieces, creating a jigsaw puzzle.

When he arrives ask him to help you work the puzzle. As this picture materializes, he will get the picture . . . and you will soon be helping him create an erotic scene all your own.

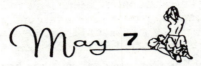

You know that the feel of silk and nylon are sexually exciting to him, but have you put to use the other materials that he also loves to feel against his skin?

Try this little thriller tonight.

Let your breasts be naked beneath a sweater made of cashmere or soft virgin wool, and ask him to dance with you. Dance close and intimately, letting him feel the soft sway of your breasts against his chest. The wool will bring your nipples to full erection and his hands will soon be slipping over your breasts. That is the time to open his shirt and let him feel the delectable touch of that soft wool against his skin.

He will soon be lifting your sweater to lap greedily at your erected nipples, and trying with words to coax you into the bedroom. Agree, but let him go first, and then remove everything but the sweater. Arrange it so that it almost, but not quite, covers your swelling buttocks, so that each step gives him a glimpse of your pubic hair. Make a slow, provocative entrance into the bedroom.

Just as the sight of naked breasts can be inviting to the man, so too can covered breasts and naked thighs and buttocks. He will soon lift that sweater to suck at your breasts as he takes you into his arms and begins loving you, but the two of you will discover that the thin bit of wool between your bodies adds greatly to your enjoyment of the act.

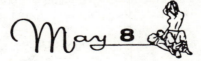

Try a bit of slow and lazy lovemaking tonight, and do it in a position especially suited for that. It is a variant of the male-behind position, and is often called "spoon-fashion."

Lie on your side, with him behind you, and the swell of your buttocks fitting neatly into the dip of his groin. Lift your leg to make his entry easier, then let it fall.

As he begins to move within you, draw his arms around your body and use your hands to guide his caresses. Try placing one of his hands over the soft, furry mound of your pubis, for he will love to feel the way this moves as you slowly grind your buttocks against his thrusting hips.

And you will love having his fingers there as you do it.

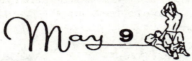

May 9

You know the tingling pleasure you feel when he takes your throbbing, erected nipples between his teeth and gently tugs and sucks them, but are you aware that he is susceptible to the same wondrous feel? Learn a little more about this tonight.

As the two of you embrace, unbutton his shirt and slip your fingers beneath it. Teasingly search out his nipples and take each between your thumb and forefinger. Be gentle as you play with them and you will feel them grow beneath your touch.

Now lower your head and begin to kiss them, taking them between your lips and flicking them with your tongue. Let your fingers clutch his penis as you do this, and encourage him to lie on his back as you continue your caresses.

Let your tongue and lips work hungrily on his now-stiffened nipples while your fingers do the same to his penis, and he will soon be white-hot with passion.

And you will be the one on your back.

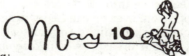

May 10

Fake a chest cold!

Tell him you have this horrible chest cold that is causing a tightness in your chest. Ask if he would mind giving you a rubdown, and give him a bottle of lotion to use. Let him apply it to your breasts. Then smile and admit that you were faking.

He will give you a healthy loving in return.

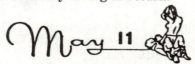

May 11

Has he ever spanked your bare bottom? Or tried to? This is one of those borderline sexual activities that excite many men and women while leaving others cold. It may be that a few stinging slaps on your naked buttocks—or the act of applying them—will be the most arousing thing either of you have experienced. Or it may leave you with a stinging bottom and nothing more.

Find out tonight.

Be girlish as you describe to him some small sin—real or imagined—that you have committed. Tell him it has bothered you all day, that you feel guilty because you have not been punished for it, and teasingly ask him if he wants to ease your guilt with a spanking. This play at "guilt" and "punishment" is usually important to those couples who enjoy spanking as a prelude to intercourse, as is the girlishness on the part of the female.

If he is really turned on by this type of foreplay, you will find yourself across his lap, the flat of his hand slapping loudly against your stinging rump; or he may give you no more than a playful slap. But in either case his hand will soon be moving across your rear in soothing strokes, and that is very close to the ultimate goal of any type of foreplay.

The thing to remember about this type of foreplay is that it is perfectly harmless fun unless taken to extremes; that is, unless it takes the place of intercourse or unless it is practiced so often and so regularly that intercourse becomes impossible without it; or unless it is allowed to become really painful.

So, with those thoughts in mind, why not be a "bad girl" tonight? The two of you may enjoy your punishment.

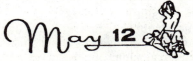 May 12

The so-called "wheelbarrow" position is one that most couples love—and for very good reason. Give it a try tonight.

Kneel beside the bed, with your panties removed, and rest your arms on the mattress in front of you. Have him stand behind you, with his feet between your legs.

Come to a half-standing position, throwing your weight forward on your arms and lifting your rear high, so that he can enter you from the rear.

When he is deep inside you, he grips your thighs and lifts your legs high, so that you can scissor them around his body. You support your weight on your hands or elbows while he grips your legs as if they were the handles of a wheelbarrow—which gives this position its common name.

This position is much easier for you to maintain than it sounds, and no position allows deeper penetration of his penis, or allows you to move your pelvis in more exotic, pleasing patterns.

Try it, and you will find that he very often asks you for "a ride in the wheelbarrow."

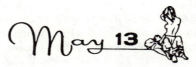

May 13

Try this extremely exotic game of fellatio and give him a thrill such as he has never before experienced!

Take six rubber bands to bed with you. Tell him he is in for the most exquisite experience of his life, and then proceed to give it to him. Have him lie naked on his back, and bring him to full erection.

Double the first rubber band so that it will be very tight around his shaft, but not tight enough to hurt, and place it around the base of his penis. Place another just above this, then another, until all six are tightly circling his penis.

Now, using only your mouth, try to remove them.

The first will be fairly easy to remove, the next a little more difficult. And to attempt to remove the next will be even more difficult, as you will have to take more of his penis into your mouth in order to reach it. By the time you have worked your way to the rubber band around the base of his shaft, you will be bobbing your lips repeatedly over the full length of his erection. These lower rubber bands, you will also discover, will move only slightly with each tug of your lips, thus causing you to work them slowly up his shaft.

The tightness of these rubber bands will also delay his ejaculation until the last one has been removed by your sucking, tugging lips—then watch out for the explosion!

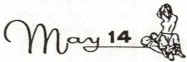

May 14

"Kiss my rear" may be an insulting phrase in most contexts, but to lovers it can also be a term of endearment; and he may be more interested than you know in placing his lips against your buttocks, or even in probing your anus with his tongue. To many men, those gleaming white mounds of flesh are the most exciting part of the female body.

Give him a chance at yours tonight.

In a standing embrace, use your hands and the aroused twisting of your body to guide his caresses down the length of your body, as if you wanted him to perform cunnilingus. Let him remove your panties and place his lips against the outer lips of your vagina, then turn in his arms, as if you were indicating that you wanted him to lick you from the rear. (This, by the way, is a very good position for cunnilingus, and is a favorite of many men.)

Spreading your thighs and leaning far forward will present your vaginal lips for his caresses, but it will also offer to him the full nakedness of your gleaming white buttocks. As he presses his face against these and searches between your thighs with his tongue, he will quite literally be invited to do anything he likes with your rear. Don't be surprised to feel his head lifting and your buttocks becoming the object of his attention; and be prepared to feel them parting as his tongue begins to dart into your anus.

After all, you invited him to do it.

This is one of the simplest and most rewarding ways to explore your own anal capabilities—and his anal desires—and it is an easy, wordless way of shedding any inhibitions you may have.

Why not turn your back on him tonight?

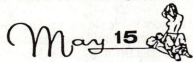

May 15

Wear the shortest micro-mini you own, with no panties, or very skimpy transparent ones, beneath it. Scatter the carpet or floor with a substance that can easily be removed, making random "stains." Then give him a brush when he arrives and ask him to clean them up for you; the idea is to get him down on his knees.

As he goes to work on the floor, you go to work on *him.*

Move about the room very casually, as if sex were the last thing on your mind, and pretend to do your housework. Let this imaginary housework require a lot of bending. Stay always within his line of vision, but just out of his reach, as your bending causes that short, short skirt to lift and reveal what lies beneath.

He will soon forget about removing those spots and begin to concentrate on removing your skirt, and you can worry about the floor later.

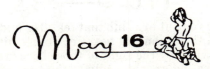

May 16

Call him at work and tell him you have just bought a "frontless, backless, topless, bottomless, strapless, evening gown," and he will quite reasonably argue that no garment of that description exists; you insist that you have one—and let him spend the rest of the day trying to imagine it.

Make him comfortable after he arrives, and tell him to wait while you put on your "gown." When you return to the room let it be just as you described it— "topless, bottomless, etc."

Be wearing a wide leather belt.

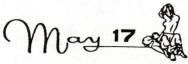

Try this oral technique on him tonight, and be prepared to hear him asking you to repeat it often during the weeks, months, and years ahead. It is a favorite of many men.

Form your lips into a soft oval and take his penis into your mouth, going as far down on the shaft as you possibly can. Then slowly lift your head until only about two inches of his shaft remains within your mouth.

Now, while your fingers move slowly up and down the length of his shaft, in the same motion you would use if masturbating him, let your tongue swirl slowly over the tip of his penis. Move your tongue first in a clockwise circle, then counterclockwise, then clockwise once again. Let your lips also move up and down over the upper part of his shaft as you do this, and increase the speed of your fingers as he begins to react. Don't forget to let those fingers move teasingly over his testicles and down into the cleft between his buttocks.

Want to give him an added thrill?

When he has reached his climax and his penis is wet with semen, continue to swirl your tongue over its tip, as if you were thirsting for the taste of his fluids. Ingestion of semen by the female is a thing many men desire, and you will find that it is almost tasteless and certainly quite harmless.

Have him take you out to a club that features nude or semi-nude go-go girls—and let those dancing beauties arouse him for you!

All men are excited by the sight of those bare breasts and buttocks writhing and gyrating unashamedly to the beat of loud, loud music, and there is no reason you should get up-tight over the way he reacts; instead, you can put his reactions to good use.

Share a drink or two with him, and perhaps a dance, while letting those hired beauties stimulate him with the suggestive movements of their semi-nude bodies, then take him home with you.

There you will reap the good, hard results of their efforts.

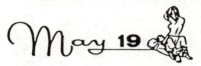

Let him enjoy an unexpected taste treat tonight!

In centuries past, it was popular among female members of royal families in France and England to apply rouge to the nipples, thus adding to their allure. You will know why this was so popular when, lifting your bra to capture your breasts, his eyes reveal his delight at the sight of your enlarged nipples.

But what about the unexpected treat?

Use flavored lipstick to darken and enlarge the circles around your nipples. Wear the same flavor on your lips. As soon as he has taken the first taste of your nipples and savored their new flavor, he will be ready to lick, lap, and suck them until not a trace of the lipstick remains.

You be ready to let him.

"Swinging" may not interest you, but the "swingers"—or more properly, mate swappers—have created many sexual games that can add to your own enjoyment. Here is a little gimmick that is very popular among that set—though, of course, they use more than two participants.

Cut a round hole about four inches in diameter in an old sheet; it should be placed about three feet from the bottom edge of the sheet. Hang the sheet from the ceiling, like a wide curtain, and have a light on your side of it, so that your silhouette is cast clearly upon it while he sits waiting on the other side.

Do a slow, sensuous strip for him, letting your hands wander over your breasts, thighs and lower stomach; then, when he is panting with readiness, turn out the light and have him step closer to the curtain. Draw his erected penis through the hole.

Your silhouette will no longer reveal the position you are taking, so you can easily surprise him with your actions. Try taking his penis into your mouth for an instant, releasing it, then turning your back to the curtain, bending, and taking the tip of it into your vagina. Next place it in the cleft between your buttocks, and quickly release it again.

Not knowing what sensation to expect next will add to the pleasure he feels and you will soon hear him gasping from the other side of that curtain.

Or tearing it down to take you in his arms.

May 21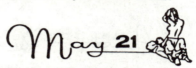

Do you recall the Ouija board craze of a few years back? These devices, which supposedly use psychic powers to answer your questions, actually use your own nervous energy to move the small pointer. But lovers can have a lot of fun with this game.

Place the board between you on the floor. Sit so your skirt is drawn up to reveal your thighs and, perhaps, a glimpse of your panties. Have him write an erotic suggestion on a slip of paper, after first extracting from him an agreement that there is to be no cheating.

Close your eyes and place the tips of your fingers on the triangular indicator. After a few moments, the nervous energy of your body will cause it to move. Let it do so until the indicator points to either the "Yes" or "No" printed on the board.

If the answer is negative, you write down a suggestion and let him take a turn at the board.

Keep playing until the answer is "Yes."

May 22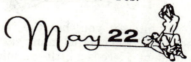

The olfactory sense can be as important to the act of love as the other senses. Incense has long been a part of erotic ritual in many Eastern countries, and it may prove stimulating to your man as well.

Buy a small incense burner and a packet of exotically scented incense today; then tonight, let its fragrance fill the room while soft music plays.

It might turn your bedroom into a temple of love.

May 23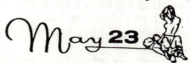

Let him find you sunbathing, and be wearing the skimpiest bikini you own, with the straps of the halter undone. This semi-nudity, which gives to him the impression of being unplanned, can be far more exciting than many more obvious costumes. You can, of course, add to the impression by sitting up to fumble with the halter of the bra, as if embarrassed.

And if he doesn't take it from there, you can always ask him to apply your tanning lotion. That will do it.

Just be careful not to give the neighbors a free show. They may not understand its loving nature.

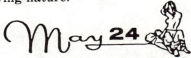

Wear a pair of long velvet gloves to bed tonight—and use them to give him some of the most incredibly delicious sensations he has ever experienced!

Your fingers are among the most potent weapons in your sexual arsenal, you know. Covered with soft, exciting velvet, fluttering over his back, buttocks, chest, stomach, penis, and testicles, they can literally tease him into sexual heaven.

It is an exciting way of creating new sensory pleasures which he will reward with vigorous, excited lovemaking, so why not give it a try?

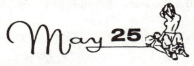

Have lunch with him today, and use that short bit of time to stimulate him in such a way that you will receive the hard results later tonight. Since the weather is right, have him meet you at the nearest park, zoo, or other outdoor place.

You order a hot dog for lunch, a soft ice cream cone for dessert, and stare hard at him as you eat. Close your lips suggestively around the end of the hot dog before taking the first bite; move your tongue sensually over the ice cream. One picture is better than a thousand words, they say, and he will soon get the picture.

He may not return to work.

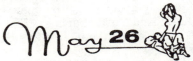

Probably because of its connection with the military, especially the military of most dictatorships, leather wear has come to be associated with sadism and masochism. But leather clothing is also exciting to men who have no such desires. Find out how it affects him.

Try wearing high-heeled, long leather boots into the bedroom, along with your skimpy underclothes. If you own or can buy them, tight leather hot-pants and matching halter, or leather bra and panties, which are available at many specialty shops, will further enhance the image you seek to create. Watch the fire come into his eyes when you enter the bedroom wearing this costume. He is most certainly not a sadist—but this will bring out the beast in him.

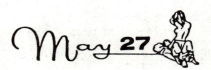

Do you remember, as a child, how wonderful it felt to run barefoot through the grass of spring? It still feels just as wonderful, and it can be even better when shared with the man you love.

Have him take a hike with you, and take it in an isolated woods where the two of you can be alone. Remove your shoes, let your hair down, and coax him into carving your initials into a tree.

You'll be surprised at how much younger you feel—and at how long the two of you remember this day.

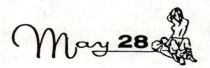

Every man and every woman, no matter how devoted he or she may be to another person, engages in a certain amount of flirting with other parties. So why not use it as an unusual form of foreplay?

Have him take you to one of those bars that caters to singles, and, by mutual agreement, spend the evening mixing with the crowd. Most of the men here are "on the make," as are most of the women; and, believe it or not, he can be greatly aroused by the sight of you dancing intimately with a stranger. And a little harmless flirtation on his part is nothing for you to become jealous about. Just be sure not to become too intimate with that stranger.

Then, at a time which the two of you have previously arranged, both of you can rise and leave the bar. By thus confirming the trust you have placed in each other, you will have strengthened your entire relationship; and at home, in the bedroom, you soon will be doing what the other patrons of that bar were hoping to do.

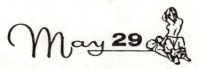

May 29

Visual erotica has remained so popular throughout history because it provides the most powerful sexual stimulus available to man, but only in recent years has it been confirmed that females are excited by it as well. And only in recent years has it become possible for the average couple, in the privacy of their bedroom, to create their own album of erotic photographs.

Start your own album tonight.

Use a Polaroid camera to take the photos, and let him direct your poses. You will learn a lot about his desires by the poses he asks you to take and by the parts of your body upon which he focuses, and he will learn the same as you direct his poses.

A timer is a great help for taking photographs of the two of you together, but you will find that it can easily be done without one. Simply focus the camera on the spot where you are going to be, fix it firmly in place, and have it close so that one of you can reach out to snap the picture.

The results may not be entirely professional, but you will find that intimate photos in which you and he are participants are far more exciting that any erotica that is for sale; and you will not only find the two of you taking down the album to enjoy it on many future occasions, but adding to it as well.

May 30

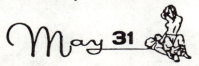

Give him an obscene phone call! There are laws against this, but not if you do it within your own home, using only the telephone extension.

Catch him when he had been napping, or has been out of the room, and tell him that some female is asking for him on the phone. Pretend to be angry as you leave the room.

Pick up the extension and breathe heavily into it. Then use a handkerchief over the mouthpiece to disguise your voice as you begin talking dirty to him. Fool him just as long as you can.

Then ask him to come into your room and be obscene with you.

May 31

The rear-entry position, especially when the man places himself over and behind the kneeling woman, is often, as you probably know,

referred to as "dog-fashion" intercourse. It is a very good position, however, and here is a cute way of suggesting it.

When he arrives, feign tiredness for a brief moment, and tell him that you "feel like a dog."

Then smile, let your hand move over his crotch, and ask him how he would like to be the dog.

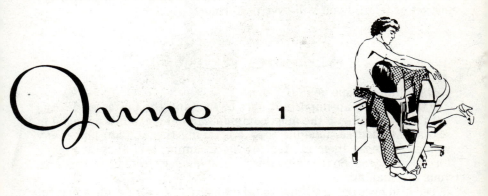

June 1

Go for a swim together. Make sure he takes you to the most deserted beach around, or to a pool that is seldom crowded, and wear the tiniest bikini you own. Let him apply your suntan lotion, and you apply his.

Then, when you are in the water, torment him by diving between his legs, letting your hands wander to the front of his trunks, even slipping your fingers inside them, if you have the chance to do it without being seen. Draw his hands up between your thighs, out of sight beneath the water, while smiling seductively at him.

He will, of course, be unable to do anything about all this, unless the beach is an extremely remote one and he will soon be wanting to leave. Make him wait until his desire becomes almost too much for him to bear.

Then let him rush you home and satisfy that desire.

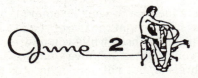

June 2

Ask him to let you bathe him—then surprise him by giving him much more than a bath!

Have him lie in the tub, on his back, and let him watch you slowly undress. Run the water until it is well up on his legs, just starting to cover his testicles and the base of his penis. Ask him to spread his legs, so that you can kneel between them.

Without a word of warning, take his penis in your hand and bend low to fellate him. Let your hair fall across his naked body, let the tips of your breasts tease his thighs, and keep your mouth sliding over the length of his penis. These sensations, combined with the luxurious feel of the water surrounding his testicles, can make this the most satisfying act of fellatio you will ever perform.

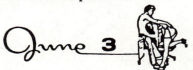

Dare him to rape you!

Fantasies are an important part of sex, and the fantasies dealing with rape are among the most common. Many men, while engaged in sexual intercourse, imagine they are raping the woman; and many women increase their excitement by dreaming that they are being forcibly ravaged. So try using this playful imagery to add new thrills to your lovemaking.

Tell him he is going to have to take what he wants, and add a playful smile to let him know it is all in fun; then resist his attempts with all the strength in your body.

You may be surprised at the passion you see reflected in his eyes as he struggles to remove the clothing from your writhing body, and you may be even more surprised at the heat you feel between your thighs as your garments are forcibly stripped away.

But most surprising of all, in all probability, will be the wild abandon with which the two of you make love—when at last you are overpowered and ready to be raped.

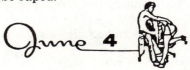

Try this tactic to add spice to your lovemaking tonight.

After the foreplay has brought the two of you to a state of simmering passion, have him lie on his back while you undress him; then let him watch as you shed your clothes. Remove your dress and bra, so he can enjoy your naked breasts, but not your nylons or panties.

Roll your panties down until they are stretched tight between your thighs, then straddle him and let him slip his penis in. When he has entered you, fall forward across his body, so you naked breasts are against his chest, then reach down with both hands and slip your panties up under his testicles, capturing them softly.

With his testicles held in this manner by the silken band of your tightly stretched panties, each twisting of your hips, each gyration of your pelvis, will be transmitted to that lowest part of his sexual organs. And you will have a good indication of the pleasure this gives when you begin to feel the tremendous power with which he lifts his hips to thrust his erection into you.

June 5

Does he ever kiss you on the mouth immediately after performing cunnilingus? And have you ever darted your tongue into his mouth only seconds after lifting it from his penis? Taste, like all the other senses, can be an enjoyable part of sex, and the taste of one's juices on the lips of a lover sometimes causes an added thrill that has nothing to do with homosexuality or any desire of a similar nature.

Why not sample that taste this evening?

Say nothing to him about it, for this is one of those sexual areas which is best entered into without discussion. Just draw him into your favorite position for simultaneous cunnilingus and fellatio; and then, when both of you are wet and approaching climax, turn suddenly in his arms and press your lips to his. Let your tongue find its way into his mouth.

You may be surprised to find, as you do this, that the taste of your own juices upon his lips gives a new excitement to his kisses; and, though he probably will not discuss it with you, the same thrill will be flashing through his mind and body.

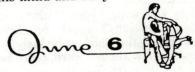

June 6

Here is a bit of nostalgia that can lead to some very, very interesting scenes; it is a verbal game that was popular about two decades ago, and it is called "In Between the Sheets."

The first player simply says the title of a song, book or movie, and the other responds with, "In between the sheets." You might say, for instance, "Love Me Tender," which is the title of an old song, and he would give the response.

Many of the titles thus created will be hilarious, but most will be extremely suggestive; but you most likely will end up playing this game exactly where it was intended to take you—"in between the sheets."

Encourage him to lead you there by giving him the title of the song called, "Take Me."

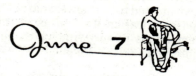

Ask him to take you on an overnight camping trip, and be sure to select a spot that is lonely and romantic. Plan the jaunt carefully, taking along food he likes, his favorite drink, and wear clothes that are tight and revealing. But take along only one sleeping bag, and be sure that it is large and comfortable.

Then share the sleeping bag with him, naked, and see that the two of you sleep as little as possibie.

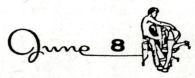

Are you interested in trying anal intercourse, but not really sure how to suggest it? Or are you not really sure just how he feels about it? Here is a silent way of suggesting it, and even if anal intercourse is a regular part of your sexual life, the technique will still be arousing to him.

Apply Vaseline or other lubricant to the anus just before he is due to arrive. Wear no panties beneath your dress, and go quickly into his arms after he enters the room.

After the first fiery kisses have been traded, turn in his arms and take his hands in yours, drawing them over your breasts. Let your buttocks weave suggestively against him as he kisses your neck and fondles your breasts; and then, without a word, reach back to grasp his penis and free it from his trousers. You will soon feel your skirt being lifted, his penis coming into contact with your naked, gyrating buttocks. Try taking his penis far between your thighs, letting him feel the lips of your vagina, then drawing away until the tip of it rests between your buttocks. Flex your muscles around him.

You will soon feel the tip of his penis pressing against your anus, seeking entry, and you can then carry the act to anal completion, or, if you prefer, turn in his arms and take your fulfillment in another manner. But you can safely bet that the fulfillment will be quick and mutually rewarding because of the prior stimulation you have provided.

June 9

Make him comfortable and giving no hint of what you plan to do, coax him into removing his shirt. Let a little time lapse, so that he will be completely unprepared, then go into another room and remove your panties.

Then ask him to take you for a piggyback ride.

Very soon after he feels the soft fur and softer flesh of your pubis against his naked skin, the warmth of your thighs around his waist, he will be riding you, all right.

But it won't be a piggyback ride.

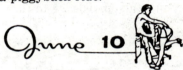

June 10

Prepare a picnic basket and invite him to share it with you, then take him to the most crowded picnic grounds you know. Be wearing a loose halter, with nothing beneath it, and shorts that are sexy but a little loose around the thighs. Be naked beneath those shorts.

To the other picnickers you will be fully dressed. But he will soon see—as you bend to serve the food, as you sit cross-legged on the ground—just how naked and lovely you are beneath those shorts and that halter. Let him have repeated glimpses of your barely-hidden nipples, of the pubic hair that becomes visible when you sit just so—and tease him with a smile when he tries to slip a finger into one of those forbidden places.

Then rush him home and give him the dessert for which he will be hungering—you!

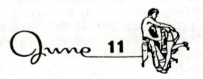

June 11

Tonight, while giving yourself one of the greatest sexual thrills you will ever experience, give him an erotic treat that he will remember for many months to come.

Use your favorite coital position to bring him to climax, but try to delay your own orgasm until after he has ejaculated. This sounds more difficult than it really is, and even if you are unable to delay your climax until after his, the result will be equally satisfying; it is important only that you be trembling with sexual excitement, your nerves ready to react to the slightest stimulus.

When he has climaxed, when you are hot and wet with his ejaculation, roll quickly free of his penis (hard as that may be to do!) and urge him to use his hands to bring you to orgasm.

Guide his fingers as they stroke your *mons*, your clitoris, the lips of your vagina, and watch the glow of excitement that sweeps over his face—if, in your rapture, you are able to see—as he brings you to one violent and all-consuming orgasm after another.

Not only is this act incredibly pleasing to most women, and not only will he derive great pleasure from his part in it, but by watching the effects of his exploring fingers, he will learn a great deal about the intricate workings of your sexual mechanicsm.

And he will gladly put this knowledge to future use.

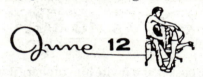

June 12

The shoes are the first item most women remove when entering the bedroom, yet, to many men, they are among the most exciting of female apparel. Take a look at the photos in any male-interest magazine and you will see that many of the girls are shown wearing high-heeled shoes, sexy hose—and little else. The publishers of these magazines have spent years and great sums of money studying the ways in which the greatest number of men may be aroused, so why not take advantage of what they long ago learned.

Tonight, wearing scanty undies that enhance and reveal the curves of your buttocks, with your legs encased in dark sexy hose, enter the bedroom wearing shoes with spike heels so high they cause your buttocks to lift and move in a new gait. Then watch his eyes!

Many men are utterly fascinated by such a sight, and you are likely to hear him asking you to parade back and forth across the bedroom while he watches the slow, sexy undulations of your rear. Do it with a smile—then parade right into his arms.

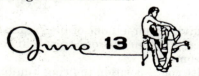

June 13

You know that sex is much better for him when you are feverish with desire and writhing in his arms, so tonight you are going to show him a sure way of creating that excitement in you.

Ask him to give you a "tongue bath"; which means, as previously mentioned, that he is to use his tongue as if he meant to cleanse each and every pore of your body. He will surely love you for suggesting it.

His lashing, licking tongue will, of course, return time after time to his own favorite areas—to your nipples, clitoris, and buttocks—and linger there, but as he begins to realize the excitement he causes as he touches his tongue to never-before-explored erogenous zones, he will grow more eager himself. And by the time your "bath" has been completed, each of you will be quivering with pure sexual energy, ready to explode.

Enjoy the explosion.

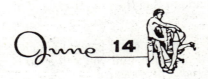

Try this unique position as a way of adding some sparkle to your lovemaking. It is one of the best variations of the male-dominant position, as it gives each of you equal control of the speed and depth of penetration during coitus.

Lie back in an armchair, with your legs thrown wide across the arms, and have him stand so he is between your legs and his knees are resting against the edge of the cushion. He should just be able to touch the tip of his penis to your vaginal lips.

You will find, however, that you can easily arch your back, using the leverage of your legs against the arms of the chair, and swing your lower body up to accept his penis. This position will allow your hips to swivel freely, taking into your vagina part or all the length of his penis, which he must drive toward you by pumping his hips. You will find that you can easily prolong intercourse by drawing away from him when he is about to climax; and you will find that having you rise to meet his thrusts makes the act even more enjoyable for him.

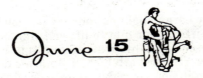

Here is an exercise designed to increase your sensuality. Try it today, and practice it regularly. It will give you a better understanding of how your body reacts to playful—and slight—pain as sexual stimulus; and by understanding this, you will also know how to provide such stimulation for him.

1. Strip away your clothing and make yourself comfortable on the bed. Use your hand or a torpedo-shaped vibrator to bring your clitoris to full erection.

2. Take your nipple between the thumb and forefinger of your other hand and pinch it until you feel the first twinge of pain. Now let your fingers relax slightly, until the pain gives way to pleasure. This is called the pain threshold, and it is different in every person.

3. While continuing to manipulate and stimulate your clitoris, use your other hand to find the pain threshold of various parts of your body.

You will soon discover the exact level at which this tiny bit of pain adds to your sexual pleasure, and you will soon be able to drive him wild by finding *his* level of pleasure.

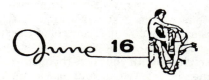

June 16

Anything that involves bodily contact also involves pleasure for a man and woman, so encourage a little bodily contact tonight by challenging him to a body-lifting contest.

Tell him you think you can lift him off the floor, but don't believe he can lift you. He will stare at you with disbelief and accept your challenge.

Bend low and lock your arms around his legs, letting him see the swells of your breasts, naked beneath a low-cut blouse, and press yourself against him as you pretend to struggle with his weight. Writhe against him for a long moment, then shake your head sadly and admit you were wrong.

Now it is his turn.

Strong as he may be, and light as you may be, you will find that you can make it very difficult for him to lift you simply by bending your knees slightly before he puts his arms around you, then allowing your upper body to relax. His first attempt, if you have done this properly, will succeed only in lifting your skirt high around your thighs as you rise to the tips of your toes. But he will overcome this with his second effort.

Then he will carry you into the bedroom.

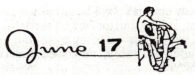

June 17

Pillows are for more than sleeping.

As you prepare to make love tonight, try placing one or two soft satin pillows beneath the small of your back, so that your body is arched upward in a delectable curve of invitation. You will find this allows you to weave your pelvis in delightful, erotic patterns that are otherwise difficult to achieve, and your lifted vagina will make it possible for him to penetrate you to the fullest.

Open final tip: If he wants to perform cunnilingus, slip the pillows beneath your buttocks and see how much easier he can perform this delicious task when you are raised to his lips.

June 18

Dress yourself in the most Oriental costume you own, one that does little to conceal your breasts and the curves of your thighs, and be sure that it leaves your midriff bare.

Then do a belly dance for him.

Sway your hips and let your pelvis roll suggestively. Draw the muscles of your stomach taut and let them relax. Turn your back to him and swivel your buttocks close to his face. Be a complete temptress. Be alluring, enticing—and ready!

Your dance need not be professional. It needs only to be highly sexual—and the movements of sex are known to all women.

You will soon be practicing those movements while naked in his arms, with both of you delighting in the exercise.

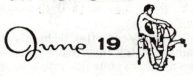

June 19

Not everyone can afford a sauna bath, but there is a way the two of you can enjoy the same stimulation. So ask him to take a steam bath with you tonight—and be prepared to enjoy the fun that will follow!

Run cold water to a depth of about one inch in the bottom of the tub, then close the curtains and run scalding hot water from the shower. Let the stall fill with steam, then have him join you in the stall.

Try using damp towels that have been chilled in the refrigerator to briskly rub his chest, thighs, buttocks, and testicles, and let him do the same to your naked body. This wll bring your skin to a rosy glow, cause your nerves to tingle delectably, and soon the two of you will be generating steam of your own.

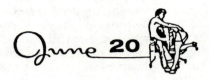

June 20

Use one of the vibrating massage devices which are designed to be strapped on the back of the hand and give the two of you the most incredible series of sexual sensations you will ever know. These devices are available at most large stores, are relatively inexpensive, and can add greatly to your sexual enjoyment.

Tell him you want him to give you a massage, have him strap the device onto his hand, and let him excite the two of you by stroking your naked body. Then guide him into one of the rear-entry positions for sexual intercourse.

When his penis is in you, guide the hand wearing the massager down over your *mons*, that soft rise above your vagina, and move it in slow circles there, pressing hard. See that both his fingers and yours touch the lower shaft of his moving penis.

The moist inner flesh of your vagina will actually seem to vibrate around him as you do this, and as you twist and writhe in orgasm after orgasm, he will be brought to a hot, explosive climax.

June 21

Playful striking of the body can often be highly stimulating to both the man and the woman, so try this little experiment tonight.

Interrupt the foreplay, form your lips into a pout, and pretend you are angry with him. Use your forefinger to playfully flick his nipple, being careful not to do this too hard, and suddenly state that you are going to turn him over your knee and spank him. Then try.

You will never be able to accomplish this, of course, but the few weak feminine slaps you give his body during the attempt can be sexually arousing.

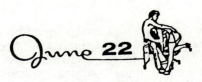

June 22

Tonight, as a special treat for him, combine oral and anal stimulation to bring him to a climax that will be gratifying almost beyond belief. The two go together like bacon and eggs.

While kneeling before him with his penis deep in your mouth, gently tease his anus with the tip of your finger; or, if you think he will not object, with the tip of one of those torpedo-shaped vibrators. As his hips begin to move faster, insert the finger or vibrator deeper into his anus, then withdraw it slowly; let your lips move over his penis with the same speed. When you feel him begin to shudder with the approach of his climax, withdraw the finger or vibrator quickly and completely, and you will taste the sudden burst of his semen.

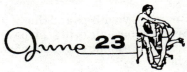

June 23

Be sitting on the sofa when he arrives, and be naked, or nearly so, beneath a very brief skirt. Have a pair of earrings handy, and very casually begin to put them on. Catch him with his head turned, make a small cry, and tell him you dropped one. Say that it rolled under the sofa, and ask him to look for it.

You do not help in the search, of course, but you will have to lift your legs to make room for him. And then, when he is on his knees and his eyes have wandered up the naked length of those legs, smile and hold out your hand—in which you are holding both earrings.

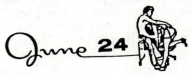

June 24

Kissing can be one of your most valuable sexual assets, and you should know a wide variety of kisses. Here is one that is extremly suggestive of oral sex. Give it a try tonight.

When he takes you in his arms to kiss you, slip your tongue deep into his mouth. Let it flicker about there until you feel his tongue forcing its way between your lips, then part your teeth slowly to accept it.

Then, when his tongue is deep in your mouth, close your teeth gently but firmly over it, holding it there. Let your teeth offer gentle resistance when he seeks to withdraw his tongue; and then, when only the tip of it remains captured, tug it slightly with your teeth. Let your hands roam his body as you do this, and vary it with other kisses, and he will soon be asking you to use your oral skills on other parts of his body—or may possibly decide to use his tongue on you.

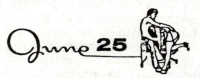

June 25

Tell him a little fib—and drive him wild!

Remove your bra and panties just before he is to arrive, then put on a thin summer dress that is *soaking wet!* Meet him at the door, laughing sadly, and tell him you were cleaning the bathroom and accidentally turned on the shower.

That wet dress, clinging to your hips and thighs and clearly revealing your swollen nipples and pubic hair, will soon have him pawing at you; and when you tell him you are going to get out of your damp clothes, he will gladly offer to help.

Let him!

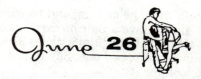

June 26

Do you remember how exciting your first sexual experience was, even though it may have been clumsy and awkward. Most women recall that first experience with a touch of awe—and so do most men.

Omitting names so no jealousy will be created, encourage him to describe his first sexual experience; and you tell him about yours.

You may find such recollections humorous; you may find them exciting; but you will surely find that such sharing and frankness is a sign of sexual maturity and mutual affection, and it does much to make your relationship more open.

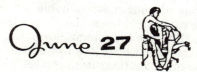

June 27

Let him open his eyes to a splendid sight!

Have a nice, heavy meal prepared before his arrival, and make him comfortable after he eats. Turn down the lights, put on soft music, and coax him into taking a nap. Then wake him up and let him find you naked, your pubis very, very close to his face, your hands drawing him closer.

Men who like cunnilingus are often extremely excited by having the woman initiate it; but even if he is shy about this, he will be enthralled by the extremely erotic thrill of opening his eyes to find the object of his love so invitingly close.

And he soon will draw it closer.

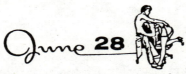

Ask him to suggest something the two of you have never done before, and tell him you are agreeable, so long as it involves no pain. Then pretend to back out at the last moment, turning down each and every suggestion he makes.

When he has grown thoroughly exasperated with this, grin and let him know you were just teasing.

Then do the very first thing he suggested.

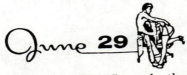

Buy a set of those "His" and "Hers" towels, then arrange for him to take you some place you really don't want to go. When he arrives, meet him at the door with your naked body partially wrapped in the towel marked "His."

Then take off the towel and let him know that the contents were correctly labeled, that you really are "His."

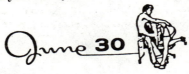

Be jealous of him tonight!

No man likes a woman who is too possessive or constnatly jealous of his casual relationships with others; but, on the other hand, a man also likes to be reminded, now and then, that you want him solely for your own; this flatters his ego.

So tonight, for the first hour or so, pout and pretend to be jealous. Let him know that you believe other women find him desirable, and men-

tion an incident that confirms this belief. Let him know that you mean to keep him for your own.

Then put on a bright, sexy smile and show him how you intend to do this.

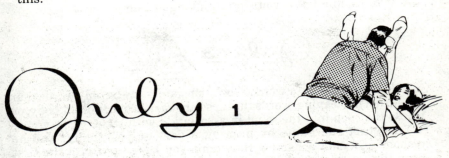

Give him an oral caress he will remember!

The underside of the penis is among the most sensitive of a man's erogenous zones, and there is a way of using your lips to create an indescribably pleasurable tingling that will linger in that area of his flesh for many, many hours.

Have him lie on his back while you lean down to fellate him to full erection. When his penis is hard and pulsing, use your hand to press it upward over his stomach, so its tip is pointed toward his face. Place your parted lips to the underside of the shaft.

Suck gently, drawing the outer skin of his penis between your lips, and then close your lips over this skin, as if nibbling it softly. When you have caught this skin with your lips, very suddenly begin to suck as hard as you can, but do this for only a moment.

This quick, hard suction will fill his penis with a delightful mixture of very mild pain and very extreme pleasure; and a small, faint red mark will remain for several hours to remind him of your lips on his penis. Make the memory even more pleasant by taking his penis into your mouth and letting your soft, moving lips and tongue bring him to orgasm.

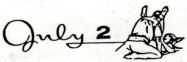

Buy one of those all-occasion greeting cards, the kind with a message saying, "Just thinking of you."

Strip yourself naked and lie on your back, the fingers of one hand touching your clitoris; then use a Polaroid camera positioned between your thighs to take a picture of this.

Place the picture in the greeting card, the card in an envelope, and mix these in with his mail.

Just to let him know you were thinking of him.

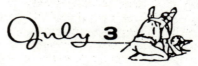

July 3

Asking him to play a word association game—using only words that are sexual in meaning, words that describe various parts of the body, or words that pop into the mind in association with these.

You start the game by naming a part of your body, and he responds—within a narrow time-limit you have set—with the first word that occurs to him. You quickly respond with the word this brings into your thoughts, and so on.

Not only is this game deeply Freudian in nature, giving the two of you deeper insight into the intimate thoughts of the other, but it can lead to some very suggestive word-pairings—and these can lead to some very interesting sexual experiments.

July 4

Independence Day

Have him take you to the nearest park and sit on the grass while watching the fireworks. Then, while the eyes of the other spectators are lifted to watch the exploding rockets, let your hand crawl up his thigh to tease him with intimate caresses. Let him feel your breasts pressing his side.

Then take him home and create a few fireworks of your own.

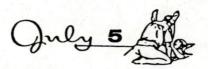

July 5

Ask him to participate in this experiment in sensory awareness.

On individual slips of paper write down as many different character traits as you can think of; one slip might read "shy," for instance, while another would say "rude." Put these slips into a box.

Each of you draw one slip from the box. Do not let him see the slip you have drawn, and have him keep his a secret. Now have him try to seduce you—while each of you assumes, as nearly as possible, the character trait on the slip you have drawn.

If each of you makes a real effort to assume these new character traits, you may well find yourself surprised by his actions—and by your responses.

This role-playing will clearly demonstrate to you just how surrounded you are by inhibitions; and, if you deeply emerge yourself into the temporary identity, it may help you to shed those inhibitions.

Why not give it a try?

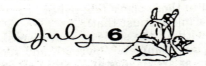

Flatter his ego by asking him to pose for a nude painting or drawing. Have the proper materials at hand and tell him you have long wanted to try to capture his tremendous physique on canvas. Persist until he agrees.

Have him strip, then coax him into assuming one pose after another, letting your hands caress his naked skin as you direct these poses. And let your caresses grow increasingly intimate.

Then put aside the painting materials and show him what an artist you can be in bed.

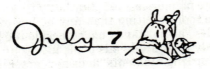

He will absolutely love this female-dominant position for intercourse, so guide him into it tonight!

Lie above him as he enters you, with your lips to his and your breasts flattened against his chest, and have your legs extended and slightly parted. Then slowly bend one knee, drawing it up until you are in a semi-kneeling position above him, and keep the other leg extended. Rock your hips slowly up and down, slithering your vagina over the length of his penis.

The voluptuous movements of your pelvis allowed by this position, you will quickly discover, will create in both of you new and astoundingly sensual sensations. They will be so pleasurable that you surely will want to feel them repeated.

So repeat.

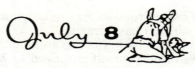

July 8

It is a simple fact of life that men are sexually aroused by looking at erotic pictures, or by reading erotic literature, and it is also a fact that many men project themselves into these scenes.

So help him project beyond his wildest dreams!

Buy him an erotic book or magazine, or a magazine featuring photos of nude females, and teasingly ask him how he would like to have the most beautiful girl in those pages fellate him.

And tell him he can have just that!

Encourage him with all the skills at your disposal. Encourage his fantasies, for they are completely normal, and remember that the photos he is looking at are images and nothing more.

And be prepared to receive in your mouth the stupendous results of all this stimulation with which you are overwhelming him.

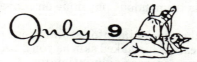

July 9

Masturbatory acts are the first type of sex engaged in by most men, and though these acts are soon replaced by sexual intercourse, faint memories of the pleasure they gave remain hidden in the mind.

Tonight use those memories, plus your hotly flicking tongue, to give him an experience more exciting than any he has ever known.

After the foreplay, as he stands naked beside the bed, sink to your knees and be greedy as you take his penis into your mouth. Let your lips move over it for long moments, and then, grasping his shaft with one hand, let your kisses move around to his buttocks. Position yourself behind him, but keep your arms around his thighs, one hand grasping his penis, the other on his testicles. Masturbate him slowly and let your tongue explore the cleft between his buttocks; let it probe his anus, which is clean and not to be ignored as a part of sex.

He may turn to have you continue fellating him, or he may stand trembling in your arms until your fingers and tongue bring him to climax—but he will surely be pleased by your actions on this night.

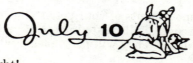

July 10

Be a virgin tonight!

Do you recall how, during the excitement of your first sexual experience, you twisted wildly, whimpering and clawing with your nails at the back of your lover? And do you remember how he loved it? He still does!

Work yourself into that same state of sexual hysteria tonight, as you are making love. Lock your legs around his body and squeeze with all your strength. Dig your nails into his buttocks, drawing him to you. Let your nails rake his back, your teeth dig into his flesh, while your hips flail wildly beneath him.

He will soon share your excitement, and you will once again feel virginal as he takes you.

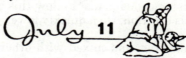

July 11

Cut the pockets out of an old pair of his pants, then be sure he wears them on the hike or picnic you are going to share today!

Enjoy the fresh air, the open country, then step up behind him at an unguarded moment put your arms around his waist, your breasts against his back, and casually slip your hands deep into the pockets of his pants. Let your fingers do the walking.

He will ask you to run—not walk—to the nearest bedroom.

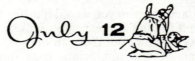

July 12

Plan a late supper tonight—the table is first going to be used for a better purpose!

Be in the dining room when he arrives. Be sexily dressed, and let the hunger for something other than food be showing in your eyes.

Be standing with your back to the table as he takes you in his arms, your buttocks resting against its edge; and then, after the first smoldering kiss, lean back, letting your pubis press invitingly against him, and encourage him to take off his clothes and take you right there!

The height of the table, you will quickly discover, is exactly what is needed to allow him the deepest possible penetration, and the standing position is one he will love.

Just be sure the table is sturdy.

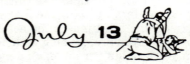

July 13

Most women think of fellatio only in terms of taking the penis fully into the mouth, yet many other oral techniques can be equally exciting. Try this one tonight.

Have him lie on his back, naked, with his legs spread wide, while you lie on your stomach between them, your face close to his testicles. Your position is similar to one he might assume while performing cunnilingus.

Touch your tongue to the lowest part of his testicles, then lick upward on them, while with your fingers you tease the very tip of his penis. Lick him three or four times in this manner, then lift your head and let the tip of your tongue move along the thick cord that runs the length of the underside of his penis. Follow this cord until you have reached the tip of his erection, then quickly lower your head and start anew.

Repeated over and over, and mixed with other caresses, this oral technique can bring a man to a stupendous orgasm—or it can be used to prepare him for a second or third round of loving.

Why not give it a try?

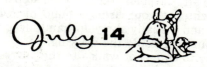

July 14

Call him at work and tell him you would like him to spend a night out with the boys—even though it means you will be lonely.

This is a good way to show your trust, to show that you are not a possessive female, and he will appreciate your thoughtfulness. Even though there exists a slim chance that he will spend this evening with someone other than "the boys," this gesture is worthwhile. For he will soon discover, as you put this book to use, that no other female can match what you have to offer.

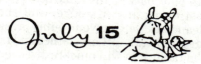

July 15

Flatter his ego tonight!

You, like most women, are probably attracted to certain male movie stars, and he certainly is aware of this. Use this to your advantage.

While embracing, or, preferably, while he makes love to you, compare him favorably with the most masculine actor you can think of, telling your man how much you prefer being with him, and how great a lover he is; tell him you wouldn't trade one moment with him for a lifetime in the arms of that ham, and make it convincing.

Then enjoy yourself as he tries to live up to your flattery.

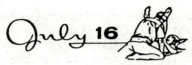

Use this experiment in sensory awareness to increase your understanding of his erogenous zones while also helping him learn more
about yours.

In a dim room, with soft music playing, have him remove your
clothing, and you remove his. Sit on the floor, facing each other, with
your bodies only a foot or so apart, and have handy a wide array of soft
items such as feathers, panties, wool, etc.

Select an item and, while he closes his eyes, slowly begin to stroke his
body, touching all parts. Then let him do the same to you, and continue
until you have used all the items.

You may be surprised to discover that he has many erogenous zones
that were unknown to you, or that he is excited by contact with certain
items, and you will also find that simple touching of the body can become the purest expression of love.

And it can lead him to express his love in other ways.

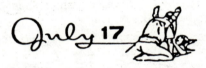

Have you avoided anal intercourse because of a fear that it might be
painful, or given it a half-hearted try and given it up without his having
made entry? Certain positions make anal entry easier, even allowing
you to control the depth of his thrusts.

Try this tonight and allow him to enjoy the pleasure caused by the incredible tightness of your anus gripping his penis.

Cover his penis and the outer flesh of your anus with a good lubricant
such as Vaseline or K-Y jelly, then have him lie on his back with his legs
together. Kneel above him, your face toward his and your anus poised
above his penis, and have him use both hands to spred your buttocks.
Lower yourself onto his erection.

Any pain you might feel will be brief, passing even quicker if you
allow the sphincter muscles to relax, and it will quickly turn to pleasure after the first penetration.

By bracing your hands on his chest and leaning slightly forward you
will easily be able to control the speed and depth of his penetration, and
you may soon find yourself wanting to feel more penis than he is able to
give.

You'll never know unless you try.

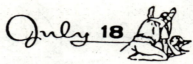

July 18

The classic position for simultaneous oral sex, often called the "69" position, is a tremendously exciting one—but the one-partner-above method is not the only way this may be done. There are many variations of this position.

Here is an exciting one for tonight.

When the foreplay has the two of you trembling with desire, let your lips move to his penis to fellate him, and turn your body, throwing one leg over him, as if to perform simultaneous oral sex while in the female-above position.

Wait until you feel his lips and tongue touching your vagina, his hands clutching your buttocks, then roll to one side, using your hand under his buttocks to take him with you, and closing your thighs softly against the sides of his face.

Resting on your side, you soon will discover, allows your hips more freedom of movement as his tongue darts in and out of your vagina, and allows him to drive his penis in and out of your throat. Small wonder that this is a favorite position among those who really understand the workings of oral sex, isn't it?

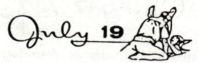

July 19

Wear a micro-mini over skimpy bikini panties, or no panties at all, and have a ladder standing in the center of the room when he arrives, a light bulb in your hand. Ask him to hold the ladder for you while you change the bulb in a ceiling fixture.

When you feel the ladder begin to tremble, and one of his hands slips under that tiny skirt, you will know he has seen what you wanted him to see.

Hurry to his arms before he knocks the ladder over.

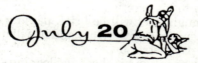

July 20

Pick three red roses today—and let him go wild while picking them tonight!

Have him wait for you in the bedroom. Go to another room and remove *all* your clothing, then use the tiniest bit of adhesive to fix one of the roses over each of your nipples, the other in the center of your pubic hair. You have created a vision that is just as appetizing to him as the nearly-nude body of the most beautiful stripper, or your own body when adorned with your most exotic lingerie.

Pause in the doorway to let him enjoy this vision.

Then smile and ask him to pluck your roses, petal by petal, using only his teeth.

If he gives you time to ask, that is.

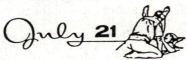

Be a little bit lewd tonight, and use your act of lewdness to give him the same psychological pleasure he derives from having you swallow his semen—or the pleasure he seeks when he asks you to swallow it.

After making love, stand as if to leave the room, then turn and smile as you stare directly into his eyes. With a wanton expression on your face, slowly touch one finger to your vagina, wink at him, and bring the finger up to your lips. Let him watch you take that finger into your mouth and greedily suck at the faint juices—which you probably will be unable to taste—then turn and walk out of the room.

You will return to find him hard and ready for another round of loving—which will make your little act of lewdness well worthwhile.

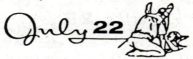

Play at being a "Lolita" for him tonight!

Wear the most girlish costume you can find. Wear no makeup, and put a large ribbon in your hair. Sit on his lap, slip your arms around his neck, and tell him that tonight you are going to be his little girl.

Then let him do all the things he would like to do to a little girl, and don't be surprised if this bit of play-acting stimulates him to a high degree of sexual creativity. Many men enjoy a mild bit of pretense, and so may you.

$$July\ 23$$

You know how excited he becomes when you use your lips, tongue, and fingers to caress all parts of his body, but have you let him feel the touch of the most exciting part of you, your pubis?

Use it tonight, to cover his body with the most unique and arousing caresses a woman can give.

Be naked, or wearing panties so thin he will be able to feel the hot moistness of your flesh through them, or wear crotchless panties, and have him lie naked on the bed. While kissing him with your lips, slowly rub your pubic mound against his thigh, causing it to grow moist, and let your hips move faster and faster.

Force him to wait while you teasingly move your hot, wet vaginal lips over his side, stomach, and chest—all the parts of his body that you can touch them to—and then be ready for the results.

And be prepared for that hot flesh to receive a few eager kisses in return.

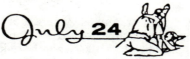

Buy a book on hypnosis. Leave it where he will find it, then lead him into a discussion of the subject, raising the question of whether a girl will submit to sexual advances while in a hypnotic state. Then ask him to hypnotize you and see.

Go quickly into "a trance."

Then, since you are under his control, you can feel free to go along with whatever he suggests.

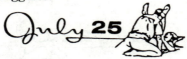

Ask him to spend a day in the nude!

Too many people ignore the beauty of the human body, letting outdated taboos prevent them from fully enjoying the joy that comes with the shedding of inhibitions about nudity. Don't be one of them.

Spend this day as you would any other, but without clothing. Go about your normal household chores. Serve your regular meals—and spend the day really enjoying the sight of your mutual nakedness. You will find it brings you closer, and several times during the day, in all probability, it will bring you so close you will be joined.

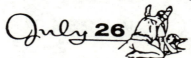

Rape him!

Tell him you are going to do so, and defy him to resist. Be wildly aggressive, throwing yourself at him and struggling to remove his clothes. Try to pin him beneath you.

Though you will not be able to overpower him with physical strength, of course, you will soon find his resistance weakening just enough to allow you to overcome it. Rape him with wild abandon.

The dream of being sexually ravaged by a female—or by a group of females—is one of the most common male sexual fantasies. You can thrill him beyond belief by innocently acting out this fantasy.

And you can have a lot of fun while doing it.

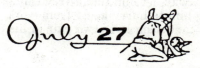

The male-dominant, or missionary position, as it is commonly known, is one that has fallen out of favor with many couples, largely because they lack the imagination needed to turn this old standby into a wonderful new experience.

Show him what you can do with this time-honored position.

As he enters you from above, lock your legs high around his back, wait until his penis begins to slip in and out of your vagina, then use your hands—and words, if needed—to still his body. Have him withdraw until only the tip of his penis remains in your vagina, then ask him to remain motionless.

Lock your arms around his neck, keep your legs wrapped tightly around his body, and use this as leverage while slowly swinging your hips up and down, around and around, to fill his penis with the most delectable sensations he has ever known.

And just wait till you feel what it does to you!

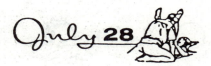

Test his sense of feel.

Have him remove his shirt and close his eyes. Tell him you are going to use your fingernail to write words on his bare skin, and ask him to guess the words you are writing. Write in a large flowery script, just teasing his skin with the tip of your nail. Begin with a few short simple words, or, perhaps, your name.

After he guesses these, which he will, if you write slowly—let your finger inscribe a very naughty message around his nipple. Repeat this over and over, and let it be something he would like to do to you.

He will get the message.

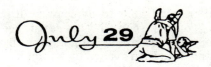

Pack his lunch for him. In a bottom corner of his lunchbox, neatly folded and hidden away, let him find a very tiny pair of your panties with a note telling him to hurry home from work.

He will do that—and soon have two pair in his possession.

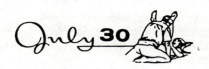

Have him take you to an amusement park. Wear sexy shorts and a halter, or an ultra-tight sweater and stretch-pants. Then ask him to take you on the roller coaster and all the other rides which encourage a great deal of bodily contact.

Follow these with a trip through the Tunnel of Love, and any other rides which will surround the two of you with darkness, and use the cover of darkness to kiss and touch him intimately with your hands.

Then take him home for some special amusement.

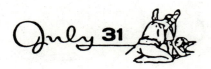

July 31

Every couple has a special language of love—little code words, phrases or terms of endearment that are meaningless to others but are sexually meaningful to the couple who use them. Give careful thought to composing a brief paragraph that will have such meaning to him.

Then call your local newspaper and have this message placed in their column of personal ads. Then sit back and relax until he sees it in the paper.

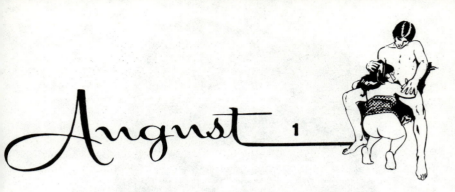

August 1

Is he sometimes hesitant about performing cunnilingus on you? Or do you sometimes feel that you do not derive from this act all the pleasure that you should? Both may be due to slight inhibitions or a lack of enthusiasm on your part rather than a lack of skill on his. Cunnilingus pleases a man by pleasing you.

Be excitingly enthusiastic about it tonight.

While locked in sensual embrace, tell him in a throaty voice that all day you have been haunted by the desire to have him do this to you, and be trembling with eagerness as he strips away your clothes and prepares to begin. Further demonstrate your eagerness by reaching down and using the first two fingers of one hand to spread your vaginal lips as he begins to kiss and lick you.

Close your eyes and try to imagine that the tongue darting in and out of your vagina is really a small wet penis, and let your hips roll as if you were copulating. This will help you to overcome any hidden inhibitions you may have about oral sex, and soon the caresses of his tongue will surpass in pleasure anything you have ever known.

You will find that as your enjoyment of this act increases and becomes more evident, his pleasure in performing it will also increase. And so will the frequency with which it is performed.

August 2

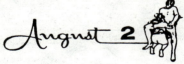

Be a harem girl tonight—and let him be your sheik.

Dress in the most Oriental costume you can put together, and be sure that it clearly reveals each enticing curve of your body. Have a good meal or an elaborate snack prepared, and use pillows to make a comfortable spot on the floor.

Tell him that you are his harem girl, have him lie with his head resting in your lap while you feed him, and then smile as you remind him of the real reason a sheik keeps a harem.

He will behave like a sheik for the rest of this night.

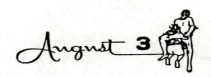

August 3

Those torpedo-shaped vibrators can be just as much fun for him as the for you.

Leave one where he can find it tonight.

He may want to use it on you, or ask to watch as you use it, but don't let him. At least not tonight. Just smile sexily and tell him you have a better purpose for it, and give him some idea of what this purpose is by running your hand teasingly over his crotch. His hardness will indicate that he is agreeable.

Have him take off his clothing and lie on his back. Use your lips and tongue on his penis for a moment, then turn on the vibrator. Place the side of it against the thick cord that runs the length of the underside of his penis, and move it slowly up and down until his hips begin to move. Then take the tip of his penis in your mouth, holding it there and moving your tongue against it, and move the vibrator faster and faster against the sensitive underside of his penis.

Soon his hands will be grasping the back of your head, his hips will be lurching upward, and your mouth will be flooded with the hot, thick flow of his semen.

And you thought those vibrators were made only for women!

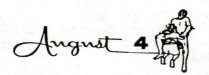

August 4

Throw a party tonight!

Invite a few couples over for drinks and dancing, and let the music be slow and soft, so you can let him feel your breasts and thighs pressing his body as you dance. Put your lips against his ear and tell him how much you regret having invited the others, how you would prefer to be alone with him, how he is turning you on.

At every opportunity, as the evening progresses, lure him to a spot where no one will see you and give him a deep, passionate kiss, letting your hands touch intimate parts of his body. This will be all the more arousing to him because he is unable to do anything about it until the others leave.

When they do, the *real* party will start.

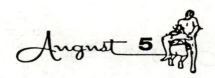

August 5

Be wearing a very sexy bikini when he arrives, and have a pair of trunks ready for him. Tell him you have been watching the wrestling matches on television, and challenge him to a match. Clear a large area on the living room carpet.

There is no way you can reasonably expect to compete with him in such a physical contest, of course, but bodily contact is the idea behind your little challenge. You will soon find, as you writhe and struggle beneath him, that he knows some very interesting holds; and you will have a chance to demonstrate a few of your own.

You will also discover that a bikini is very easily removed and that a carpeted floor can be a very interesting place for making love.

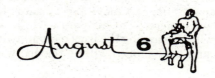

August 6

Tonight, as a part of the foreplay, try bending down suddenly, without his asking, and covering the length of his penis with delicate, loving kisses. Cradle his erection in the palm of your hand and let your soft lips show your appreciation of it by caressing it until it pulses and throbs with readiness.

If you are one of the few women left in this world who has allowed old taboos against oralism to cause you to deny him the pleasure of fellatio, this is a good way to break the ice and begin shedding those inhibitions, and tonight is the time to do it.

After a few kisses on that hard erection have shown you how harmless this act really is, and have revealed to you the pleasure he derives from it, you may find yourself eager to take his penis into your mouth and finish what you have started. Do so, by all means!

Even if fellatio is a common part of your sexual play, you will find that he loves to suddenly find his penis being kissed by your lips, and even though you may not wish to continue fellating him on this night, you will surely be repaid for your thoughtful caresses when you spread your thighs to accept the hard results of your loving foreplay.

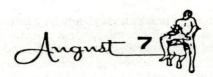

August 7

It is a strange fact of sexual psychology that mild fetishism is relatively common among men, but almost unknown among women. And it is also a fact that such fetishism is harmless unless it is allowed to take the place of, or interfere with, the normal sexual functions.

Hair, shoes, leather, female undergarments, and rubber clothing are among a few of the items to which, to widely varying degrees, men are likely to form a sexual attachment. In most men it is hardly proper to call this a fetish, for they feel only a vague sense of sexual excitement at the sight of the fetish-object, without quite realizing why.

Draw him into a conversation about mild fetishism tonight. Let him know that you are aware of the above facts, that you are interested in satisfying his deepest desires, and coax him into telling you a few of the things that secretly excite him.

You may discover that your hair is the part of you most exciting to him, or he may want to see you dressed entirely in black leather, or perhaps he is fascinated by your breasts; he may even express a secret wish to place his penis between them and copulate to ejaculation, which is a common desire among men who have a mild fixation on the female breasts.

And, of course, he may not admit to any such secret sexual urges, or he may be unaware of their existence. But at least the conversation will have taken a turn toward the sexual, and the hours that follow will prove that sex is a better topic than politics.

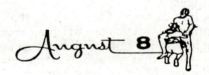

August 8

There are many Freudian reasons why men are excited by the sight of the female breasts, but these are of little interest to you. You want to know *how* he is excited, not why he is excited.

Try this bit of enticement tonight.

As he lies on the bed or sofa waiting for you to join him, do a slow, sensuous strip, stopping when you are left wearing only your panties and bra.

When it is off, and with your eyes still locked on his, use your hands to lightly rub those red marks always left by a bra, sighing with pleasure as you do this. Put your hands against the outer curves of the soft spheres and press them together—and watch the look of desire that comes into his eyes. Stay out of his reach as you continue.

Cup one breast in the palm of each hand and lift them, as if for his inspection, then give them a squeeze. Use the thumb and forefinger of each hand to gently pluck at your nipples, and slowly move your hips as you do this. The sight of a woman bringing her own nipples to erection is very stimulating to most men, and he will now be literally begging you to come to his arms.

When at last you do go to him, try lifting your breasts in your hands and holding them to his mouth as he sucks and licks them, just as if you were nursing a baby: once again, for psychological reasons, this is highly stimulating to most males.

And it will, of course, be just as stimulating to you.

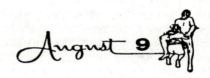

August 9

Many men are strongly attracted to women who are sexually insatiable, or to women who are nearly so. It is this strange attraction which will sometimes cause an otherwise intelligent man to remain devoted to a cheating wife.

Be insatiable tonight!

Lead him into a furious bout of lovemaking that begins with cunnilingus which continues until you are writhing in orgasm, and follow this by taking him into your vagina. Tell him repeatedly, while in the midst of these acts of love, that you simply cannot get enough of him— and demand that he satisfy your sexual hunger.

After his first climax, be voracious as you use oral stimulation to renew his erection, and cry out with desire as he once again thrusts his penis into you.

If you are like most women, and if he is like the average man, your orgasmic potential will be far higher than his, thus allowing you to continue this almost indefinitely. But you are likely to discover that your sudden sexual insatiability creates in him a state of excitement that allows him to satisfy you beyond your wildest dreams.

Time after time after time.

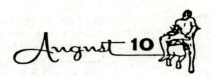

August 10

How well do you sew?

It really doesn't matter, because your sewing skills are the last thing in which you want him to be interested. But you can use these skills, however weak, to bring a smile to his face and an erection to his penis.

Sew a naughty message on the seat of your panties. Make it one that makes an explicit sexual request. Let it begin with his name, and follow this with, "I want you to. . . ."

Wear the panties under your shortest skirt. When he arrives, clumsily drop something on the floor in front of him, then take your time as you bend over to retrieve it.

He will read you . . . loud and clear!

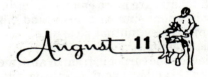

August 11

Tonight treat him to this exquisite bit of oral-anal stimulation, and at the same time let him know the wonderful wetness of your vagina, with its soft surrounding hair, against his skin!

When the foreplay has brought the two of you to a state of quivering readiness, and after he has removed your panties, use your hands to coax him into a prone position on his stomach, with his legs slightly parted. Use your hands and lips to stroke and caress his naked back, finally bringing your lips down to the hard muscles of his buttocks. Turn on the bed as you do this, then lift one leg and throw it over his body, so you are sitting astride his shoulders, your face toward his feet.

Bend down and let your lips and tongue move over his buttocks as you use your fingers to spread them, and press your *mons* against his back, moving it and letting him feel your hot wetness against his skin. Lower your face between his parted thighs, letting your tongue seek his testicles, and then bring it back up to flick hotly around his anus, or into it. Again, keep in mind that the anus is clean and free of fecal matter, and dip your tongue as deeply into that tight circle of flesh as you wish.

He will soon be turning to take you with incredible vigor, as no man can long endure this combination of sensory stimulation. But you will be perfectly happy to endure the loving he gives you in return!

Buy him a cigar!

Give it to him the moment he comes in the door, and congratulate him on his approaching fatherhood. After a stricken moment, he will ask you when the baby is due.

Smile sexily, kiss him, and tell him it will be at least nine months from now, since the two of you are just getting ready to start its conception.

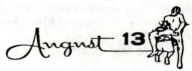

Cunnilingus and fellatio are more enjoyable for both the performer and the recipient when done simultaneously, and this is a terrific position in which to enjoy these mutual pleasures!

Give it a try this evening.

Place a large pillow on the carpet in front of an armchair, and lie with your back resting on this pillow, your legs thrown wide and across the arms. Your buttocks should be lifted high and resting against the front of the chair.

As he moves over you and bends down to use his lips and tongue on your enticingly lifted vaginal area, his penis and testicles will be conveniently placed to receive your own caresses. And you will find that he uses his hands on your buttocks to draw your body into an even more dramatic bow, his tongue to lap at you as he has never lapped before. Be prepared for the tremendous climax his eagerness and your oral skills will cause.

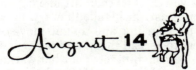

Here is a little secret that will make you especially appealing to him at that critical moment when he is ready to make love. Why not give it a try tonight?

When the foreplay has created a fiery need for relief in the two of you, and he is eagerly fumbling with the last of your clothes, slip out of his arms and strip to your panties, bra, and hose.

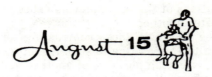

August 15

Stand just out of his reach and keep a provocative smile on your lips as you slowly, ever so slowly, tug your panties down over your hips. Stop when the upper half of your pubic hair is revealed.

Turn slowly and tug the flimsy panties down until they are taut across the undercurve of your buttocks, making a deep crease in the rounded flesh. Let him enjoy this alluring picture for a moment before once again turning and easing the panties down a little more, to reveal all of the flesh and downy hair for which he hungers.

And don't be surprised if he grabs you and begins making passionate love to you while the panties still encircle your thighs; many men find this state of semi-nudity even more arousing than the sight of the totally naked body.

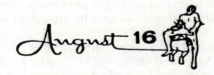

August 16

You may know that certain changes in temperature on the erogenous zones can be used to give him a higher degree of sexual pleasure, but are you also aware of how they can stimulate *you* to new heights of orgasm? Here is a technique that will allow you to experience one such thrill while at the same time offering him a sexual experience that plays on several of his senses.

Wearing a sexy, flimsy negligee that you can part to reveal a tiny bra and crotchless panties, take a book into the bedroom and one or two cans of ice cold beer. Tell him you are going to read for a bit, and ask if he would care to join you. He will.

Sit with your back resting against the headboard of the bed, and pretend to read, letting the negligee carelessly part to reveal your excitingly clad body. After a moment or two, casually take a sip of the beer, then tilt the can, "accidentally" spilling a few drops of the cold brew on the pubic hair that is revealed by your exotic, erotic underwear.

Teasingly ask him if he would like to drink the beer from your body, then, without giving him a chance to reply, spread your thighs and pour a little more of the cold liquid over your vagina.

As the cold liquid seeps down over your vaginal area, you will find that the shock of it brings your clitoris quickly to a full erection; and as he licks and sucks at you with his warm mouth, you will find that the contrasting sensations of warmth and cold cause you to undergo one violent orgasm after another.

He, too, will be aware of those contrasting temperatures as he presses his mouth to your vagina to suck from it the flowing liquids, and he will be experiencing pleasure of another nature. The desire to take food or fluid from the female vagina is not uncommon among men, and it is this desire to which you are catering.

Just have plenty of beer on hand.

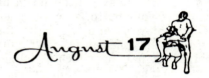

Make him your sexual servant for the evening!

Hidden deep within every man, no matter how masculine he may be, is the latent desire to be dominated, if only temporarily, by a sexually demanding woman. Let that woman be you. And let tonight be the night!

Meet him at the door with a stern but loving expression on your face and tell him that you have decided it is time he began catering more fully to your sexual needs. Demand, in your most serious voice, that he commit an act which you know is especially appealing to him, and use a scolding voice to instruct him in how it is to be done.

Then make him repeat the act, and tell him to do a better job of it. He will.

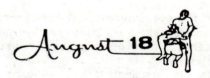

On this date in 1932 the first convention of the Liberty Party was held in St. Louis, Missouri. Tell him that you intend to celebrate the anniversary of this historic event by having a "Liberty Party" of your own.

Such a party is simplicity itself. Just smile as you slip your arms around his neck, kiss him deeply on the mouth, and move your pelvis suggestively against him; then tell him that, because of the great significance of this date, he can take any liberty with you he likes.

This may well become his favorite holiday.

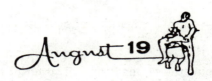

August 19

You know how he loves to take the pliable softness of your breasts in his hands and stroke and fondle them, and you are surely aware of the pleasure he takes from covering them with his mouth and tasting of them, but are you aware of the many other ways in which your breasts can be used to give him sexual pleasure?

Watch his face glow as you try this one tonight!

Have him lie on his back, naked, with his penis fully erected, while you kneel so his penis is directly beneath the cleft between your breasts. Put your hands on the outer curves of your breasts and press them inward, capturing his penis between the delectable swells of flesh. Move them so that his penis is rolled slightly by the softly enveloping spheres.

Now take his penis in one hand and gently ease the outer skin down as far as it will go; then, even more gently, for this is a very sensitive area, use your fingers to spread apart the "eye" at the center of the head of his penis, the small opening through which he ejaculates.

Let your nipple move teasingly around this small opening a few times, and then, using the fingers of your other hand to guide it, try to insert your nipple into this opening.

Though very sensitive to pain, which means you must exercise caution, this is one of the most potent erogenous zones on the male body. By toying with it in this manner, by letting him feel the delicious probing of your nipple, you will have brought him to an incredible state of arousal.

Now enjoy the results in any manner you like.

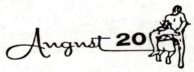

August 20

Stimulate him to a second round of lovemaking—and do it without speaking a word!

After you have finished making love, and before he has had a chance to close his eyes, stand as if preparing to leave the room, then pause and stand with your thighs slightly parted, the finger of one hand casually, but enticingly, pressing against the soft mound at th top of your pubis.

The pressure of your fingers will cause a slight bit of his semen to seep from your vagina and trickle down your thighs, and in the instant before you leave the room, you will see a renewal of lust glowing in his eyes.

Though this may sound vulgar or even repulsive to you, the sight of seminal fluid escaping the vagina is sexually exciting to most men, and he will be ready to replace the bit that escaped when you return to his arms.

August **21**

Make arrangements to rent a boat and have him take you for a ride on moonlit waters.

Romance is just as important to him as it is to you, though he may be slower in expressing his need for it, and what could be more romantic than sharing a summer night on the lake?

Make it a night to remember by spending as much of it as possible in his arms, talking of love, and drifting where the currents take you as you share the beauty of the stars above.

Your relationship may well become as beautiful as those stars.

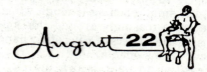

August **22**

Try this extremely satisfying technique of fellatio tonight.

After using your lips and tongue to bring him to full erection, use your fingers to draw the smooth outer skin as far up over the hard inner core of his penis as it will go. Draw your lips down over your teeth, form them into a soft oval, and slip them down over his penis until you are just able to capture these folds of skin.

Let your lips open and close over this skin in quick little tugs, almost as if you were a fish gulping for air. This will cause his skin to slip back and forth over the sensitive tip of his penis; and by using your knowing fingers on his testicles, and occasionally letting your tongue swirl hotly over other parts of his penis, you will quickly bring him to an explosive climax.

August **23**

Be a little bit of a tomboy . . . but not too much of one.

Go out and buy a bag of marbles, then return home and put on a blouse cut so low that it scarcely covers your nipples, a skirt so short and tight that you might as well not have it on.

Then challenge him to a game of marbles, out in the yard, and agree upon a sexy, mutually enjoyable penalty the loser must pay.

You will find, as you kneel in the grass with your blouse falling away to reveal the swells of your breasts, your ready-to-be-tasted nipples, that he is totally unable to concentrate on the game.

He wll even be in a hurry to lose it!

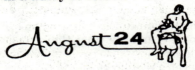

August **24**

Here is an exercise in sensuality that will increase your potential for anal eroticism. Try it today, and practice it regularly.

1. Lie nude on the bed, facedown, and spread your legs wide. Let your hips move slowly, pressing the mound of your pubis against the sheets until you begin to feel aroused.

2. Now, without slowing the roll of your hips, take a large fluffy feather—the type once used to make those boas—and draw it teasingly over your buttocks. Part the buttocks and touch this bit of softness to your anal entry. Now let your buttocks close over the soft curls of the feather, holding it there.

3. Continue to create a delicious clitoral stimulation by moving your pubis against the sheets, but try to concentrate on the soft caress the feather is bestowing on your anus. Try to bring yourself to orgasm by this method.

You may be quite surprised at your reaction to this exercise, and your man will be delighted with your new awareness.

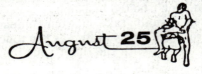

August **25**

Challenge him to a test of skills he will really enjoy.

Use your hands, kisses, and body language to encourage him to take a position suitable for simultaneous oral sex, then look teasingly up in-to his face and bet him that you can cause him to reach orgasm before he can cause you to do the same.

Each of you is to try to delay orgasm as long as you possibly can, but make it against the rules to withdraw from the mouth of the other as a means of doing this. This is a sex game in which the loser need not pay a penalty.

But he or she should certainly be allowed to have a rematch.

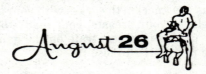

Take a look at the letters to the editor in any of the largest of the male-interest magazines and see what they can do to stimulate your sensuous imagination.

Unless you have been a regular reader of this particular part of these magazines, you are going to be surprised to discover that the letters have become the most sex-oriented part of these publications; in them, readers describe, in very vivid language, every type of sexual experience ever conceived by the human mind. Some may strike you as grossly perverted, others as merely boring, but a few will give you ideas of your own.

These are the ones to which you now direct his attention.

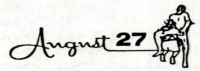

Although they say it is impolite for a lady to apply her lipstick in public, today you are going to do it—and it is going to be the most suggestive thing he has ever seen.

Use a toothpick to carve the tip of your lipstick into the shape of a penis, then call him at work and ask him to have lunch with you. During the meal, try to talk him into taking the rest of the day off and spending it with you. Don't be too insistent.

Then after the meal, casually take out your compact and the penis-shaped lipstick. Stare suggestively at him as you touch it to your lips, and let him see you taste it with the tip of your tongue.

He won't be going back to work.

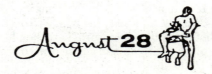

How often have you stimulated him anally as a way of adding to his sexual pleasure? Most men find such stimulation highly pleasurable,

though not all women are aware of this, and you should use this fact to your advantage.

Tonight use it to add new power and fervor to his lovemaking, and see how your body trembles in delight as you feel his thrusting penis go deeper than ever before!

Let him remove your panties but keep them close beside you, and encourage him to take a position that places him above you, with his face toward your own. Take the panties in your hand as he enters you and reach around to grasp his buttocks, letting him feel the soft, exciting silk against his skin. Caress his rear with the silken garment and slowly move the caresses closer to his buttocks.

Now cover one finger with the panties. Use this finger to tease that circle of flesh for a moment, until his thrusts become more passionate, then insert the silk-covered finger into his anus, taking with it the sheath formed by the panties. Let him enjoy the feel of your finger a moment, then ease it carefully out, leaving in his anus the bit of silk you inserted with it.

When the increasing speed and depth of his thrusts warn you that he is within a second or two of his climax, slowly, very slowly, ease the silk out of his anus.

And be prepared for the explosion about to take place deep in your vagina.

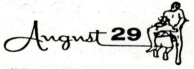

August **29**

Show him how well he measures up.

Visit a well-stocked bait and tackle shop, or sporting goods store, and buy one of the so-called "liar's rulers" or "fisherman's rulers" that you will find in these stores.

These novelty items look exactly like a regular ruler, except each "inch" is only half as long as it should be, thus allowing a fisherman to "double" the size of his catch.

Now use this ruler to measure his penis—and enjoy yourself as he happily puts his increased length to work.

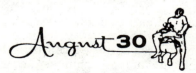

August **30**

Why waste a good chair by just sitting in it? Why not show him tonight how his favorite chair can be used to provide new sexual thrills for both of you?

Have him sit in the chair, naked, while you slowly remove your last garment in order to make love. Then turn your back to him, sink slowly down over his lap, and use the fingers of one hand to guide the tip of his erected penis to the warm lips of your vagina.

Pause for a moment, letting him enjoy the feel of only the tip nestling there, then lower yourself fully onto his shaft. Guide his hands around to cover your breasts. Put your own hands on the arms of the chair and use the leverage this provides to slowly lift and lower yourself over the hard shaft of his penis.

He will never again think of that chair in quite the same way as before!

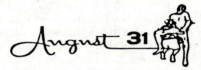

August 31

Buy a hula hoop, and let him come through the door to find you wearing your sexiest bikini and twirling the hoop around your waist and hips with the sensual undulations this requires. Then ask him to join you inside the hoop.

You will soon discover that it is almost impossible to keep the hoop going while the two of you are inside it; but you will also discover that most of his efforts are being directed toward getting you out of that bikini.

Give him a little help.

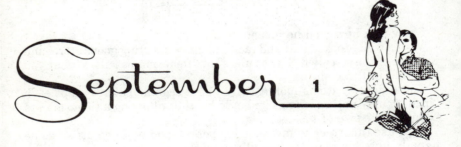

September 1

Good autumn weather is here, and it is the perfect time for a little healthy exercise that can also be sexually arousing.

Ask him to go jogging with you.

Wear no bra. Let your breasts move freely beneath a loose—but not *too* loose—sweater. Hold hands with him as the two of you run until you have worked up a sweat. Then, of course, you will each need a shower to wash away the perspiration.

Which should cause him to start sweating again.

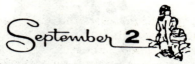

September 2

Here is a bit of visual stimulation that can be almost as exciting as a bedroom lined with mirrors. Give it a try.

Place several dim lamps on the floor, so they will be in a rough circle around the spot where you will be standing. Draw him into close embrace, then lead his attention to the multiple shadows cast on various walls.

As he undresses you, as his hands and lips caress your breasts and thighs, as he enters you and begins making love, each motion will be repeated again and again in dim silhouette around the two of you.

He, too, will repeat them again and again.

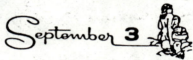

September 3

If he is like most men, he is subject to anal stimulation, as you now know, though he may be somewhat reluctant to admit it; and he may express displeasure at any attempt to actually thrust your finger or another object into his anus.

But he can be anally stimulated without actual penetration.

Prove this tonight.

Take a large, soft feather to bed with you and playfully tease his body with it. Let the teasing lead to loving, and let the feather be briefly forgotten.

Then, when he is between your thighs with his penis thrusting deep into your vagina and his lips covering the tips of your breasts, take up the feather and let him feel it caressing his naked back. Move it lightly across his skin to his buttocks, and use your free hand to spread these wide. Let the feather touch the circle of his anus until you feel him react by plunging deeper into you, and then try letting his buttocks close over it.

You will find that feathers are good for something other than mattress stuffing. Very good.

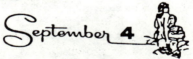

September 4

A change of position always brings new vigor to lovemaking, so tonight suggest this position as an exciting contrast to those you normally use.

When the two of you are ready to make love, when he is naked and fully hard, have him kneel on the bed with his legs together and his buttocks resting against his heels. Have him lean back slightly and use his hands against the bed to support himself.

You then kneel in front of him, but your thighs are wide apart. Keeping his legs between your own, and lifting yourself as necessary, move over him and insert his penis. Then *you* lean slowly back. When you feel his penis begin to withdraw, lean forward again, and continue to use this rocking motion until the two of you are shaking with orgasm.

Although movement is somewhat restricted in this position, the movement that is allowed is such that it causes some of the most exquisite sexual sensations imaginable. Give it a try.

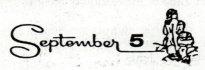

September 5

Tell him you are going to test his skill as a lover. This is one test the two of you are going to love.

Tonight, when he begins to make the sexual advances which you are going to encourage, tell him that you read someplace that a truly skillful lover should be able to bring a woman to orgasm without actually entering her vagina—either with his penis, his finger, or his tongue. Then dare him to try.

He will gladly accept.

During the prolonged foreplay that follows, with his lips and fingers caressing your nipples, buttocks, your navel, and even the soft *mons* area of your pubis, he may or may not bring you to orgasm. But he will stimulate the two of you to such incredible heights of passion that the orgasms which follow will leave you stunned.

And both of you will be surprised at what a skillful lover he really is—when *you* encourage him to be.

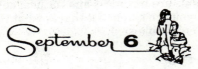

September 6

Tonight give him a tingling bit of sex he will never forget!

If you have not already done so, buy one of those flat, vibrating massage devices which are designed to be strapped on the back of the hand. As stated, they can be found at most large department stores, are relatively inexpensive, and can be used to give the two of you many hours of sexual pleasure of different types.

Wear this device tonight—and very little else—and give him a slow and very sensual massage. Then massage him in a way that will give him a pleasure he never dreamed possible, and be just as pleasurable to you.

Encourage him to stand and enter you from behind. Let him fill his hands with your breasts as his penis begins to move. Then use your own hands to drive him wild.

Press the hand wearing the vibrator flat against the soft *mons* area of your pubis and hold it there, letting the tingling reach through your soft flesh to surround his penis. Then move the hand lower and let it touch the shaft of his thrusting penis, filling it with vibrations that you also will be able to feel. Reach far back and take his testicles in your hand, then let your fingers move slowly back to the point where you began.

Just don't count on these voluptuous sensations continuing for a great length of time, for very soon you will feel yourself receiving the full length of his driving penis.

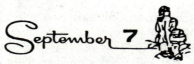

September 7

Ask him to play peeping Tom!

There is a bit of the voyeur in every man, and the trait is completely normal. It is largely for this reason that magazines featuring photos of nude females have been so successful, and is surely why visual erotica has lasted through the centuries despite all efforts to suppress it.

Cater to this natural and harmless male tendency by asking him to describe exactly what he has always secretly wanted to see you do, and by telling him you will do it.

He may want only to watch you dress, or to see you wearing certain sexy items, or to have you pose in a certain way; but don't be surprised or offended if he wants to watch you masturbate, or use a vibrator on yourself. These things are harmless and natural so long as they are a prelude to sex, and you can safely bet that is what they will be—a prelude to some very enjoyable sex!

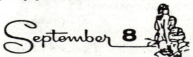

September 8

You know how sexually aroused he becomes when, in the midst of a tight embrace, you slowly grind your pubis against his rising erection; but how often have you used the soft, sleek curves of your buttocks for the same purpose?

Put them to work tonight. You'll be surprised at his reactions.

Have soft music playing, and ask him to dance with you. Let him get fully into the mood encouraged by the music, then turn your back to him and draw his arms around your waist. Turn your face for a kiss and keep your body swaying in time to the music. Press your buttocks tight against his crotch and let them roll provocatively.

Soon you will feel his penis rising to full erection against your rear, his hands easing their way toward the hem of your skirt, and he will be whispering soft suggestions in your ear.

Take him up on these suggestions.

September 9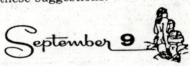

Give him a milk bath!

There was a time when a bath in a tub filled with milk was thought by many to be the ultimate luxury; but even today, who can afford all that milk? You can!

After telling him what you intend to do, have him go into the bathroom, remove his clothes, and wait for you in the tub. Then join him, totally naked, and have in your hand a small bottle of milk. It will be all you need.

Kneel in the tub between his legs and pour the milk over his nipples, penis, and testicles, smiling sexily as you pretend to scrub his body. Then let him do the pouring while you use your lips and tongue to catch the flowing liquid. Stay at it until not a trace of milk remains on his skin.

He will readily agree that a milk bath is still the ultimate luxury.

September 10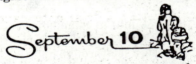

Ask him to join you for a walk. When you are as far away from home as you intend to go, ask him to stop for a moment. Do this at a busy spot, with people passing by.

Teasingly reach out as if to touch his lips, then slip the tip of your finger into his mouth and touch his tongue. Tug playfully at it, if you can, and let your eyes drop suggestively downward. In the same tone of voice that you might use in discussing the weather (which means you will go unnoticed by those passing by), openly and brazenly tell him how you love the feel of that tongue, and say you wish he could use it on you at this very moment.

Such public boldness (though it is not really bold and will go unheeded by those around you) is very exciting to most men—and you can expect a few heads to turn as he rushes you home to do the things you have been suggesting!

September 11

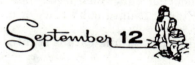

Try this approach to analism tonight.

If you have still found little excitement in your attempts at anal intercourse—or even if you practice it regularly and find it enjoyable, as huge numbers of women do—this approach to the act will make the first entry easier and increase, for both of you, the enjoyment analism can provide.

Have a jar of lubricant such as Vaseline, or K-Y jelly, on a table beside the bed. When he is hard and erect, and your panties are on the floor beside you, reach out for the jar of lubricant; he will know what that gesture signifies.

Tease his penis with your fingers as you cover it with the lubricant. then smile and roll over onto your stomach, and put the jar in his hands. He will take it from there.

As he uses his finger to apply the lubricants to your anus, you will feel your muscles relaxing, your anal desire increasing; and when you rise up on your knees to accept the first thrust of his hard, slippery penis, you will find your state of readiness is higher than ever before.

And his thrusts will be deeper than ever before!

September 12

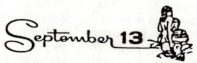

Call him at work and ask him to come home for lunch, telling him you have prepared a very special meal for him—then prepare it.

Put on a pair of sexy hose, a see-through nightie . . . and nothing else. Wait for him in the bedroom.

Call to him in a sultry voice when he arrives, and be waiting on the bed when he enters the room. Then try to talk him into extending his lunch break for the rest of the day.

You will find that it requires very little talking.

September 13

Do you find yourself unable to overcome the gagging that is caused by your attempts to swallow his semen, a thing that most men desire as a part of fellatio?

Try this "sweet" way of overcoming that tendency.

Take a jar of honey to bed with you and spoon the thick sweet liquid over his penis, after telling him what you intend to do; he will gladly go along, as he desires this far more than you.

Take as much of his erection into your mouth as you possibly can and suck hard as you move your lips over him. Try to imagine that the thick fluid you are drawing from his penis is really his semen; since the two are of similar consistency, this will be fairly easy to do. You will find that you lose the tendency to gag as you repeatedly draw the thick honey-semen into your throat, and you may be unable to tell the difference when it changes to the real thing.

September 14

Rid yourself of an inhibition tonight!

If you are like most women, you have certain sexual desires which go unfulfilled because you are too inhibited to even talk about certain acts, much less suggest trying them. Perhaps you simply want to try a unique sexual position; or it may be analism or exotic oralism which intrigues but eludes you. All of us have such hidden desires.

Bring them out into the open by attributing them to another person. Tell him that a girl friend (real or imaginary) described to you a sexual experience that really thrilled her. Give him the same intimate details this friend supposedly gave to you, and tell him you were surprised to learn she was excited by such things.

Your own interest and excitement, try as you might to keep it hidden, will be telegraphed to him; he will come to the defense of the friend in your story, insisting the act is perfectly normal, and soon he will show you how normal—and how much fun!—it is.

And you will go to sleep satiated, and with one less inhibition.

September 15

Have him take you to a nearby playground!

Wear a very short skirt, one that clings to the curves of your hips, and no bra underneath a thin blouse. Head straight for the swings as soon as you arrive at the park. Swing high only when he is directly in front of you, giving him his favorite view, and then ask him to push your swing. He will.

But soon you will find his hands pushing against your buttocks rather than against the seat of the swing, and his voice will be suggesting that you retire to another playground—the bedroom!

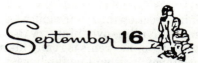

September 16

Your fingernails, as you are probably well aware, can be used to tease and excite him in many ways. Drawn lightly over his face and neck, moved over his scalp, tracing a line around his nipples, or digging into his neck as you make love, they add greatly to the sexual excitement created by other parts of your body. But you may have overlooked the most exciting way of all in which your nails may be used.

Give this a try tonight.

Encourage him to take a position above you, and lift your legs to lock them tight around his waist. Let him penetrate your vagina and begin to move; then, by placing one hand against his chest or stomach and squeezing with your legs, stop his movements just as his hips are lifted and only the tip of his penis is in you.

Holding him there, slowly and tantalizingly use the tip of one fingernail to draw a line from his stomach down the length of his penis until your finger reaches the point where he vanishes into your body. Then let your legs relax, and he will begin to move once more.

Stop him after a few plunges of his penis and once again use your fingers to trace the line down his penis. He will soon get the idea and pause regularly to hold himself poised for your teasing finger.

But after a few repetitions, neither of you will be able to stop.

Nor will you want to.

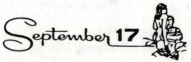

September 17

The water at the lakes, beaches, and pools is now cold enough to be far more stimulating than in early or midsummer and the crowds have long since vanished, so challenge him to share a swim in the icy waters. Wear a bikini that will be far more breathtaking than his first plunge into those cold depths, and be sure to take along plenty of soft warm towels which you can use to rub away his goose pimples.

But rub them in an intimate way designed to give him more.

September 18

You are aware, of course, that the best way to add variety to your lovemaking is to use a wide assortment of sexual positions, but how often have you tried changing positions during the actual act of intercourse? It is a beautiful way of showing your man that you are aware of his need for sexual variety.

Try this combination tonight.

Let intense foreplay culminate with you above him, your legs around his thighs and holding them together as you take his penis into your body. Press your mouth to his and let him feel your nipples against his chest as your hips begin to move, and stay in this position until his upward thrusts become quick and passionate; then, break the kiss and draw your knees up, one at a time, to bring yourself into a sitting position over his penis.

Lift yourself slowly, until only the tip of his erection remains within your vagina, then turn and bring your face around toward his feet, your buttocks toward his face. Listen for his gasp of delight as he watches your vagina move slowly down to reclaim the full length of his hard erection.

September 19

The female breasts probably hold the greatest sexual attraction, for the greatest number of men, of any part of the body, and their importance should not be overlooked by you when you are fellating him. Tonight is the perfect night to show him how wonderful they feel against his naked skin while your lips and tongue are licking, tugging, and sucking at his penis.

Wear a short, transparent nightie which parts at the front and let your breasts be lusciously naked beneath it. Let him sit on the edge of the bed to remove his clothing. When only his shorts remain, drop to your knees in front of him, let your gown part in the front, and remove that last article of clothing for him.

As you bend low to tug the shorts over his feet, let the tips of your breasts sway against his legs. Take his penis in one hand and, holding it tight, bend low and begin kissing and licking the insides of his thighs, letting your naked breasts sway against him as you do this. Lift your head until you are able to lick with your tongue at his testicles, and with one hand urge him to lie back on the bed. Move over him and take his penis in your mouth, then circle his thighs with one arm, so they are held tight against the soft, sleek cushions of your breasts.

As your clinging lips move over the hard shaft of his erection, drawing him ever closer to orgasm, the incredibly soft breasts he feels touching his thighs will be but one more reminder of how fortunate he is to be with *you*.

September 20

Play an old game with an exciting new twist!

Bingo is a game everyone knows, and it may become your favorite pastime (or at least a frequent prelude to your favorite) after you try playing it this way.

Follow the regular rules, but remove one article of clothing each time a number is called that appears on your card, and have him do the same when one of his is called. Not all numbers appear on all cards, so the game will be longer than you might expect. The first to cover his or her entire card (and all your clothing will be shed long before this happens) decides what sexual "penalty" the loser must pay.

Bingo!

September 21

Here is a household "chore" he will love!

Dress yourself fully from the waist up, but have on only a long apron below your waist. The apron should cover you fully in the front, but leave your buttocks naked and alluring.

Be in the kitchen when he arrives, and have the sink filled with suds. Stand facing him and ask if he would like to join you while you do the dishes. Then smile and turn your back.

He will soon "join" you.

But neither of you will be doing dishes.

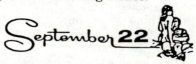

September 22

You can add immensely to his enjoyment of the sexual act by using unexpected pauses to prolong it until his body is quite literally shaking with the need for release. Find out how well this works tonight.

Guide him into the male-above position and let him enter you; and then, when his penis begins to slip quickly in and out, lock your legs tightly around his waist and use them to stop the motion of his hips, stopping him when his shaft is almost totally withdrawn.

Hold him still for a moment, with only the tip of his penis nestled between your vaginal lips, and keep your hands and mouth roving over his body. Let your pelvis swing upward after a long moment, again covering his penis with your soft warmth, and he will respond with a bucking of his own hips.

Stop his movements again and again in this manner, each time allowing him to come a little closer to his climax, and soon you will find you are unable to stop him.

But only because you lack the willpower; not because you lack the strength.

September 23

Have him take you to dinner at a nice romantic spot—and use this little trick to show him how romantic you feel!

Excuse yourself for a trip to the ladies' room. Remove your panties and put them in your purse. Then return to the table, smile suggestively, and let him see the contents of your purse. Grin and say you were suddenly too hot to wear them.

He will soon be even hotter!

September 24

Entering you from the rear is often far more enjoyable for him if he is standing, and in a position that allows him to drive his hard penis at you with maximum force, so tonight try offering yourself to him in a way that presents just such an opportunity.

When he is hard and ready, when your panties have been removed, rest your folded arms on the back of an armchair, so that your buttocks are toward the front of it, where he is standing. Now place one knee on each arm of the chair, lean forward, and lift your buttocks high.

Your legs will be spread wide, allowing him easy and full penetration, and you will be poised at exactly the right height to receive his thrusts. The mobility of your hips in this position will allow you to weave your vagina before him with perfectly sensuous fluidity, and his hands around your waist will provide additional leverage as he buries himself sensuously in you.

Time after time after time!

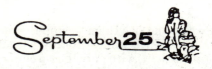

September 25

Fellatio is probably the sexual variation he most enjoys, if he is like the great majority of men; and this act, too, should be varied in as many ways as possible. Repetition can cause even the most exciting technique to lose some of its sexual potency, so why not try adding a little dash to your oral routine tonight?

Kneel over his naked body and close your fingers into a tight fist around the base of his erected penis. Squeeze hard and tug upward, at the same time covering the tip of his shaft with your mouth. Continue to squeeze and tug as your lips engulf his penis, then let your fingers relax as your lips slide upward. Tighten the grip of your fingers as your lips again go down.

Your tightly grasping fist will not be painful to him; rather, it will be a delectable contrast to the gentleness with which your lips cling to his throbbing erection. Fellatio should be a combination of many skills and techniques, and this is one technique that he will really enjoy—either as a prelude to intercourse or as a means of bringing him to a heated climax.

September 26

If you haven't been able to overcome your reserve and are hesitant about having him make anal contact with you; or if you are unsure of his feelings about this type of sex, tonight is the night to use this simple method of overcoming your hesitancy. Even if you are anally experienced, it is an experience you will love to repeat.

Use your hands, lips, and body language to encourage him to perform cunnilingus on you, and have him do it from a prone position between your parted and naked thighs, his face directly in front of your vagina.

Arch your back and lift your buttocks at the first touch of his lips. As his tongue begins to flick into your moistened flesh, reach down to find his hands and guide them under your buttocks, so he is holding you lifted to receive his kisses. Keep your hands in contact with his.

As you writhe against his caressing lips, use your hands over his to show that you want your buttocks spread; and after a moment, if he still has not slipped a finger between them, twist your hips until your anus makes contact with one. That will give him the idea.

As his finger slips into your anus and his tongue continues to flit across your clitoris, the combination of sensations you feel will match in pleasure anything you have previously known; and as your excitement transmits itself to him, you may find his tongue lashing out to join his finger in that cleft between your buttocks.

But in any case, you will find that this is a terrific way to make even more enjoyable an act which is already one of the most exciting of all—and it could pave the way to enjoyment of an act you have been hesitant to try.

September 27

This exercise in sensuality is designed to teach you more about your own orgasmic functions. A better understanding of your own potential for orgasm will make you a better lover when you are with *him*, and there is no better way to reach this understanding than through occasional masturbation.

Try this exercise today and practice regularly.

1. Strip away your clothing and make yourself comfortable on the bed. Relax completely. Let your fingers manipulate your nipples until full erection is achieved. Then slowly begin to manipulate the *mons* area of your pubis, bringing the clitoris to full erection, and continue until orgasm has been reached. Now try to achieve another orgasm—and be prepared to learn a lot about yourself!

2. The clitoris after orgasm, in many women, becomes extremely sensitive, even painful, to the touch. A *pause* is usually needed before more pleasure can be obtained. Other females experience no such sensitivity, with orgasm being almost continuous, and have no need to pause after the first climax.

3. Begin to stroke yourself, giving in to all sensations lazily. You will soon become excited again. As you control your orgasm with your own fingers, learning more and more about your own sexuality, you may discover that you are able to adjust your potential for orgasm to bring it in line with your sexual desires.

And that is a goal worth striving for.

September 28

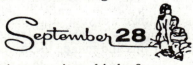

Does he like having you sit on his lap?
He will after tonight!
After long and passionate foreplay during which you use every sex-

ual device you know to bring him to quivering arousal, allow him to strip away all your clothing (with the possible exception of your nylons, as you choose), and you remove his.

Have him sit on the edge of the bed, or in a chair, with his legs slightly parted. Turn your back to him, then ease yourself down over his penis, settling into his lap. Draw his hands around to cover your breasts as you begin to move up and down over the hard shaft of his penis.

Now reach down and carefully use the fingers of both hands to spread your labia, the outer lips of your vagina, wide. Release them and let them close tight around him once more. Spread them once again, and gently insert the tip of one finger, lightly touching it to the shaft of his penis. Release the labia once again.

After repeating this a few times, with your vagina moving up and down the length of his erection, you will feel his hands leaving your breasts and slipping down to join in manipulating your soft vaginal lips and clitoral mound. And this will take place only seconds before you feel a tremendous upward thrust of his penis and the spewing warmth of his climax!

September 29

Too many women confuse fellatio with masturbation—doing little more than holding the tip of the penis between the lips while using the fingers to bring the male to ejaculation—but there are ways in which, done deliberately and knowingly, this technique can be used as an incredibly delightful variance of oral sex.

Tonight is the night to try a few of them!

Kneel over him and take his erected penis lightly between the tips of your fingers, and let him see you smile provocatively in the instant before you touch the tip of your tongue to it. Swirl your tongue over its tip, and let your fingers slowly manipulate the smooth outer skin of his penis. Take only the tip of it between your lips and hold it there as you increase the speed of your fingers. Make a fist around his shaft and move the fist up and down, letting your breath play over his flesh.

Don't forget to use the fingers of your other hand to caress his testicles and buttocks, and continually vary the strength with which you grasp his penis. Use your lips and tongue to caress his shaft, but concentrate on the many ways in which you can give him pleasure with your fingers. Then make it a totally erotic experience for him by covering his penis with your mouth at the last possible instant and capturing the hot flow of his semen.

September 30

Most males thoroughly enjoy the act of cunnilingus. The ability to bring a female to orgasm after orgasm by using only the tongue and lips is thought by many males to be the mark of a truly skillful lover, and the act of doing so is almost as exciting to the orally-oriented male as it is to the female receiving his caresses.

But just as many men prefer a sexually aggressive female as a partner in intercourse, or prefer to have intercourse take place with the female in the dominant position, certain men prefer having the female take the aggressive role, or the dominant position, during cunnilingus.

So be totally dominating tonight!

When the foreplay has advanced to the point of no return, and you are naked in all the areas that count, suddenly throw one leg across his body and offer your vagina to his mouth—not in a position you would take if you were going to return his oral caresses, but in one that places you astride his head, your vagina directly over his face!

As he lifts his head between your thighs and begins to caress you, let your pelvis twist and roll, moving your vaginal lips wetly against his face, and don't be afraid to use your hands to hold his face tight against your flesh, or to lower yourself and press hard against his sucking mouth.

Such actions signal to him how greatly you are aroused by the feel of his tongue and lips, and you soon will feel him attacking your flesh more eagerly than ever before.

Be sure to reward him for his efforts.

October 1

The rear-entry position is a common one that almost every couple knows. Many women find that it provides greater clitoral friction than any other position, thus increasing their enjoyment of sexual intercourse, and you may be one of these. And while he probably enjoys this position as well as you, there is a simple technique that can be used to make his pleasure even greater.

Give it a try tonight.

Have him stand and enter you from behind as you lean forward at the waist, resting your hands on the edge of the bed. Let him move in and out of you until you are warmly lubricated, then have him remain motionless. You take it from there.

Let your hips undulate slowly before him. Move them in intricate circles, squares and figure-eights, and reach back with your hand to fondle his testicles. Let your body then begin to rock back and forth, sliding his penis in and out, and be prepared to hear him moan with pleasure as he revels in the luxury of having you provide all the movement of copulation.

October 2

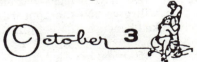

Use a silk scarf to thrill him beyond belief!

Tonight, while he waits for you in the bedroom, tie a large silk scarf around your breasts, making a bra of it. Be sure the silk is thin enough to give a clear view of your nipples. Enter the bedroom wearing this "bra," your panties and hose, and nothing else.

When he takes your breasts in his hands and covers your nipples with his mouth, the touch of the silk will be exhilarating to both of you, and you may be tempted to keep his lips at your breasts forever. Don't. The scarf can now be put to a better use.

After he has removed your panties, untie the scarf and, moving over him, hold it in your hand as you reach down to grasp his stiff penis. Hold the scarf over his shaft and slowly masturbate him as you draw his penis toward your vagina. As the tip of his penis enters you, release his shaft, leaving the thin scarf around the base. With each deep thrust the two of you will feel its sleekness between your bodies, encouraging even more passionate lovemaking.

October 3

Ask him to take you for a drive.

Wear a short, sexy skirt that will slip even higher on your thighs when you are seated in the car, and be sure to place yourself very close to him. Let him get a good distance from home, and then, when he is stopped for a light, very casually put your hand in his lap and squeeze him. Do this at every traffic light, letting your language become as bold as your hands, and soon you will find the car headed in the oppostie direction.

Be sure he stops for all the red lights.

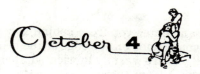

October 4

A second, or even a third, erection is easier for him to achieve than you might think. Please him tonight by showing him how easy it can be—and please yourself, of course, while doing it.

After making love for the first time, go into the bathroom and prepare two washcloths. Run very cold water over one and warm, but not hot, water over the other.

Return to the bedroom and let him feel your naked body touching his as you use the cold washcloth to wash his penis and testicles, letting your fingers grip and squeeze him as you do this. Then, very abruptly, switch to the warm washcloth. You will see the first renewal of his erection as your fingers move the warm cloth over his penis. Now switch back to the cold cloth, and move it over his penis until he has adjusted to the change in bodily temperature, then once again cover his penis with a feeling of warmth—but this time let it be the warmth of your mouth.

He will be ready to repeat your previous actions.

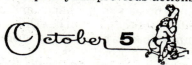

October 5

There are laws against public nudity, but there is a way that you can fill his mind with vivid images of your naked body even while you are in a public place, and you can do so while staying well within the limits of the law.

So why not show him how daring you can be?

Dress in a very short, very tight, very sexy skirt; and wear hose that draw his eyes to the loveliness of your legs—but omit the blouse and bra. Wear a jacket that will give you the appearance of being fully clothed, but be utterly naked beneath it. Meet him at the door and ask him to join you for a walk.

At the first opportunity after you have left home, when you are in a spot where no other person can see you, smile provocatively at him and open the jacket as far as you dare, giving him just a glimpse of your naked breasts and stomach. Then close the jacket and go on with your stroll.

The knowledge of just how near to nudity you really are, and yet how innocent you appear to those passing, will seem just as daring and exciting to him as if you actually were nude in public, and his mind will be filled with the memory of that one brief glimpse of your naked breasts.

And when you return home, be sure to give him a chance to

demonstrate what a gentleman he is by allowing him to help you out of your coat.

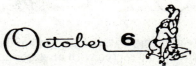

October 6

Show him the place he occupies in your thoughts!

Embroider his name on one pillowcase and yours on another, or, if both your names are commonplace ones, buy two pillowcases with the names already sewn on. Have them on the bed, side by side, when he arrives, and smile as you invite him to try them out.

This is one of those simple shows of affection that can be of such great importance to the relationship between a man and a woman, and it is the type of thing that can be the difference between love and lust. Use this way of showing him the permanency of your feelings toward him, and you will be pleasantly surprised to discover that he will begin to seek little ways to display the affection, and love, he has for you.

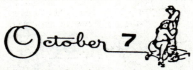

October 7

Do you find that the male-dominant, or man-above, position for intercourse has grown almost boring because of overuse? This variation of it will allow his penis to penetrate you more fully than ever before and will add new spice to this old standby position.

When the two of you are naked, or nearly so, and ready for love, draw him over you and between your parted legs, but use your hands to encourage him to remain rather low on the bed, with his face at about the level of your upper pubis.

Now lift your legs and let them fall high around his body, then grasp his upper arms and urge him toward you. As he moves over you, let your lower legs or ankles find a resting place on his shoulders; they will rise almost straight into the air, and your buttocks will be lifted as he moves to enter you.

Let your knees bend and adjust until you have found the posture that is most comfortable for you, and use your hands on his back and the cheeks of his buttocks as he begins to plunge.

Though this position allows very little movement of your lower body, and though you may at first find it awkward, these minor disadvantages are more than compensated for by the tremendous depth of penetration it makes possible.

That is something both of you will enjoy.

$\mathcal{O}$ctober 8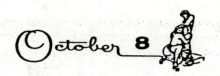

Many men dislike dancing, but this is a kind of dancing he will love!

Place several records on a stereo with an automatic record changer. Have several different types of music, but be sure all are suitable for dancing. Let him know you have something up your sleeve, but not exactly what.

Dance close to him, letting him feel your breasts pressing against his chest, your pubic mound against his groin; then, when the record changes, smile sexily and remove one item of your clothing, one item of his. Resume dancing, and continue to remove one item of clothing with each new song.

Soon you will be dancing in your skimpy undergarments, feeling the hardness of his erection against you; and not too long after that, of course, both of you will be naked.

But it is highly improbable that you will be dancing!

$\mathcal{O}$ctober 9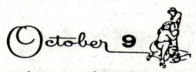

Bodily contact is an important factor in any sexual position, and no rear-entry position offers more contact than the variation to which you are going to introduce him tonight.

As he lies with you on the bed, his hands and lips caressing your naked breasts and pubis, turn onto your side, pressing your buttocks against his groin, and reach back to grasp his penis. Let him enter you from the rear and begin to move before taking the next step.

After his penis has begun to slip steadily in and out of your vagina, slowly, very slowly, draw your knees up toward your breasts, curling your body into something similar to a fetal position. You will feel his legs bending to follow yours, and the strokes of his penis will come faster and faster.

With his chest, stomach, and upper groin pressing against your naked back, his arms around you and his hands holding your breasts, and the back of your legs against the front of his, this position allows the two of you to more fully enjoy the feel of flesh against flesh than does any other rear-entry position. And you will find that by straightening your legs, then bending them once more, you can delightfully alter the angle at which his penis enters you—a good addition to an already excellent position!

October 10

Be a country girl tonight!

Wear a pair of bib overalls with the suspender straps carefully arranged so they cover the tips of your breasts—and be absolutely naked beneath these.

Go about your housework as you normally would (though you will be dodging his grasping hands) and let him sit there enjoying the sight of your swelling breasts as they bob and sway against the straps that are too narrow to contain them.

The female breasts are at their most beautiful when displayed in this manner, with only the tips of them hidden and only the slightest bit of restraint, and the almost casual manner in which you are revealing those alluring spheres to him this evening will cause him to hunger for them as never before.

When you find his arousal is such that you are no longer able to keep his hands from sliping under those straps, or no longer want to, be a good little country girl and join him in the hay!

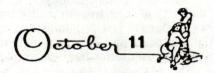

October 11

Here is a position that is strictly for fun; but fun, after all, is what sex should always be. So have some fun tonight!

When your clothing is on the floor and he is hard and ready, have him sit with his legs stretched out and slightly apart. You then take a sitting position over his penis, facing him, with your legs over his thighs and extended behind his back. Press your lips to his and let him feel your naked breasts before beginning the act of love, and do this until he is trembling with eagerness.

Place your hands on his shoulders, and guide his hands to yours. Lean slowly backward, and have him do the same, until you are holding each other with outstretched hands. Now fall back, pulling him by his hands, and then, when he is drawn to an erect position, have him fall back and pull you up.

Rocking back and forth in this manner will cause his penis to glide in and out of your vagina with incredible slowness that is all the more delicious precisely because it is so slow.

October 12

Give him a scare tonight!

Put a slight bit of padding under your clothing, directly over your tummy, and touch it with your hand as you meet him at the door. Smile weakly, tell him that you have good reason to suspect that he is going to become a father, and hand him a strong drink.

Give him time to finish his drink, then kiss him and quickly remove the padding as you admit that you are not really pregnant.

Then tell him how much you would like to start working on it!

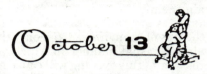

October 13

You are not a lesbian, of course, or you would not be so interested in him and what you can do to please him. But there is a little-known fact distantly related to female homosexuality that you can use to increase his excitement as he makes love to you this evening.

While most men are repulsed by male homosexuality, it is true, oddly enough, that the majority of them are enthralled by the idea of two women engaged in sex. Visions of female homosexuality are one of the most common sexual fantasies had by men; such scenes are often staged as a means of sexual stimulation by those couples who engage in mate-swapping and group sex; and to this fact can be attributed the success of erotica portraying lesbianism. Put this fascination with the subject to work for you and see how he reacts.

Tell him that during the day, while in a cocktail lounge, you were approached by a lesbian. Tell him she openly made sexual overtures, and lead him into a discussion of the subject. Let this discussion center around the question of how lesbians satisfy their sexual needs. Even though he is fully aware of your heterosexuality, he will be creating in his mind, even as he discusses this with you, images of nude female bodies writhing together. These fantasies may or may not place you in the mental arms of another female, but that is unimportant.

In response to your questions regarding the manner of female homosexual intercourse, he will respond, as most males would, that it is achieved through cunnilingus—and you can safely bet that he will offer to demonstrate.

And he will do a better job of it than any lesbian could do because you love him!

October 14

Before he is due to arrive, apply Vaseline, K-Y jelly or another good lubricant to your anus; then use an easily removable ink to scribble across your skin, just above your pubic hair, a few words that will insure his use of your ready anus.

Dress skimpily and sexily, draw him into a heated embrace that will end with your few garments removed and his penis hard and throbbing against you, and let him discover the message written above your vagina.

"This door closed," it will tell him. "Please use rear entry."

October 15

A woman's hair, if she uses it properly, can add an exciting ingredient to her performance of fellatio. Try using these techniques tonight as you use your lips, tongue, and mouth on his penis, and you will have a very satisfied man sharing your bed.

Have your hair loose, so that it falls about your face as you bend to kiss, lick, and suck at his erection. Deliberately move your head so the soft ends of your hair move teasingly over his stomach, penis, and testicles. Try turning your face to one side and pressing it against the shaft of his penis, so a bit of your hair is trapped between his skin and yours.

If your hair is long enough, try taking it in your hand and holding it lightly around his penis, moving it up and down, while with your lips and tongue you caress the tip of his shaft.

He will demonstrate by the ferocity of his climax that you have fellated him as he was never fellated before.

The female hair holds sexual meaning for all men; in a few of them, it even becomes a fetish, a fixation. This is because the hair of the mother is one of the first things of which the male child becomes aware. Though this lingering memory is very faint in most men, and he may not even be aware of it, it is there.

And for that reason your hair is a beautiful and powerful sexual instrument you should start using tonight.

October 16

By varying the rear-entry position for sexual intercourse so that he is above you and thrusting his penis down into your vagina, you also change the angle of penetration and the parts of your inner flesh that are touched. Why not a new angle tonight?

The sofa is the perfect place for this position, though using it means he will have to stand with his knees slightly bent—which he will be more than glad to do.

Lie face downward on the sofa, with your stomach resting on the arm at one end, and have him stand between your parted legs as he enters you from the rear. When his penis is in and deeply probing, have him lift you by the thighs and step closer to the end of the sofa, so his penis will be angled down as much as possible.

This position also increases the friction against your clitoris, thus adding to your own enjoyment; and causes greater contact with the sensitive underside of his penis, adding to his own sexual excitement.

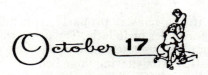

October 17

Pantyhose, as they come from the store, must surely be one of the most drab and unappealing female undergarments ever conceived, but tonight you are going to surprise him by turning a pair into one of the most erotic pieces of apparel he has ever seen.

Use a pair of scissors to cut the crotch from a dark-colored pair of pantyhose. Use clear nail polish to paint a line around the edges of the opening, which will prevent further tearing, and allow this to dry before donning the hose.

Wear a skirt short enough to reveal your thighs as, during the course of the evening, you bend or sit with crossed legs, and you will soon have him wondering what happened to your normally sexy hose and garters. But he will stop wondering when at last he takes you in his arms and slips one hand under your skirt to be surprised by the soft hair and naked flesh that lies waiting at the center of your creation.

Wear the hose while making love, and let him thrill to the sensuous touch of nylon-clad legs that caress even his hips and buttocks as he plunges into you.

You might even sell this design to the hosiery industry!

October 18

Kissing is, of course, one of the most important displays of affection and quite possibly the most important prelude to sexual intercourse. Your kisses should be both loving and suggestive, and they should cover not only his lips and face, but should be used to explore his erogenous zones as well.

Tonight let your kisses concentrate on one such area that is too often neglected—and see what he gives you in return!

After the first moment of kissing, while he holds you tight in his arms, let your lips move around to his ear. Kiss him softly there, letting him feel your hot breath, then take the lobe between your lips and tug it gently. Nip him just hard enough to cause pleasure but not pain, and then let your extended tongue swirl over his ear, darting in and out.

This highly arousing form of kissing is one most women know, but unfortunately, as the relationship with a man grows comfortably familiar, too many of them tend to let their kisses assume a dull sameness, forgetting the excitement a man can feel as he feels the touch of lips and tongue to his ear. Don't you be one of these.

He will thank you for having remembered!

October 19

Be a blabbermouth!

Pretend to be on the telephone when he arrives. Laugh and giggle a lot, and let him hear you mention the name of a girl friend he knows as you talk into the dead receiver. Start describing, in this one-sided conversation, the last time you had sex with him, and capture his attention by using his name often.

Use vivid detail as you chatter about what he did to you, how wonderful it felt, and the intimate things he said as he was doing this.

He will soon put a stop to this by taking the receiver from your hand, and he will then discover your little hoax.

And he will give you something else to talk about!

October 20

In common slang, sexual intercourse has been referred to—

somewhat vulgarly—as "A roll in the hay." That term, however, could be used to describe one of the most beautiful sexual techniques in existence.

Give this technique a try tonight!

Let your foreplay bring him to full hardness and excite you until your vaginal fluids are flowing freely, and let him remove your bra and panties. Move over him while he lies on his back, and place your legs outside his as you settle yourself over his erect penis. Cover his mouth with your own, letting him feel your naked breasts against his chest as the two of you begin to move, and then slip your hands under his shoulders. Squeeze him with your thighs.

Now roll to one side, drawing him with you, and never letting his penis slip free. Use this delectable position for a moment, with your hands moving down to his buttocks and pulling him deep, and then turn again, until he is over you and driving hard between your thighs.

Now turn again, in the opposite direction, pause once again on your side, and once again bring yourself up over him, where the slow but steady pumping of your hips will let your vagina slide up and down the hard length of his penis.

Not only does this technique add to the enjoyment of sex by combining three positions with no interruption in the pace of your lovemaking, but you will find that each roll of your sexually-joined bodies causes the hard rise above his groin to press against your soft clitoral mound—with an exquisite friction that causes each of you to be filled with a feeling of rapture.

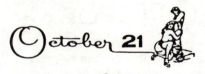

October 21

Just as some men are sexually excited by the sight of naked female breasts, or by the buttocks, others experience great arousal when confronted by a female wearing exotic hosiery, a matching garter belt— and nothing else. Entire magazines have been devoted to, and have flourished by, catering to the male fascination with the female legs.

Show him how lovely yours can be!

Carefully select the most exotic pair of nylons you can find, and add a garter belt designed only to arouse. Very dark hose, or ones made of broad, net-like mesh, are what you want. Wear these under a sexy skirt, and spend the early hours of the evening letting him use his imagination to attempt to visualize you as you would appear without that skirt—and that is exactly what he will be doing.

Let him go to the bedroom first. Make him wait while you remove your outer clothing, your bra and panties, and don't just walk through the door of the bedroom—make an entrance!

Give him a seductive smile as you pose with your hands on your hips, your naked pelvis thrust forward to tempt his eyes with the soft fluff of your pubic hair, and turn slowly to let him see the garter straps that hug your hips, the way your naked buttocks contrast with the material of the hosiery that stops just beneath them.

When at last you go to him let him feel those nylon-clad legs writhing around his naked body, and don't worry about ruining them during your frenzied lovemaking.

What he gives you will be worth more than any pair of nylons.

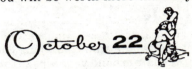

Perhaps the best feature of the male-above position for sexual intercourse is the fact that he is facing you, and can use his hands and lips on your breasts, while also seeing at least part of your lovely, undulating body. Perhaps the worst feature is that too many couples do not attempt to vary this position in any way.

Here is a variation that retains the best of what the standard technique has to offer while adding some new thrills all its own, and here also is an easy way of getting him to try it.

Sit on the edge of the bed as you remove your panties and he removes the last of his clothing; then, when he is naked, take his hand and coax him into standing between your legs. Then laugh teasingly as you fall back on the bed and lock your legs high around his naked body, trapping him there. Throw your weight back on your shoulders and arch your back, lifting your pubis toward him.

His hands will soon settle under your buttocks, or you can guide them there, and that will be followed by the first deep thrust of his erect penis.

This standing position allows him to watch each excited twist and turn of your lovely, and exciting, body, as his penis slips in and out of you. It has the added allure of letting him witness the expressions that sweep over your face as you reach orgasm after orgasm.

Which is exactly what you will be doing.

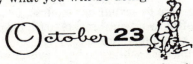

A bikini can be useful, even when the weather is too cold for swimming.

147

Wear the skimpiest one you own today, and cover it with a winter coat just before he arrives. Then ask him to go for a walk with you.

Now try to convince him that you are naked beneath the coat; give him quick glimpses of bare flesh, and laughingly tell him you think you forgot something. Try to keep him from discovering the truth. He will hurry you home to see if you are as daring as you pretend to be, and will, of course, see that you were not really naked.

But you soon will be.

Buy a very small lock, and a thin chain long enough to circle your waist and hips. Fix the chain around your hips so the tiny lock is centered over your pubis, and cover this with a pair of transparent panties.

Tell him you are locked into a chastity belt, and when he expresses his disbelief, let him make his own inspection.

Then smile and hand him the key.

Buy two tickets to a football game featuring one of his favorite teams. Make it a night game—and plan on taking along a blanket large enough to cover both of you, and protect you from the chill air and the eyes of those around you. Plan on sharing a lot of intimate contact beneath that blanket, and have a victory celebration after the game.

Even if his team loses!

Tonight, as a prelude to sexual intercourse, or as a part of fellatio, use the delicious softness of your breasts to fill his penis with exquisite sensations he will remember forever.

Have him lie on his back while you bend over him and tease his penis into full erection. Place yourself in a kneeling position, as if you were going to fellate him, then draw his penis into the cleft between your naked, dangling breasts. Use your hands to press the soft globes around the tip of his penis.

Now move your shoulders up and down. Use your hands to move your breasts in opposite directions, rolling the tip of his penis between them. Vary the speed of your movements. The delectable softness of your breasts around his penis will soon have him ready for anything—but he may be reluctant to have this pleasure cease.

Use this easy way of shedding a few inhibitions tonight!

Ask him to take a nap with you. Pretend to drop off to sleep as soon as you are snuggled up against him, and then start "talking in your sleep."

Let him hear a few jumbled words about the one form of sex you have been too inhibited to try but have always secretly desired to explore. Mention his name. Express pleasure.

Though not as good as being completely open about your sexual desires, this technique will make it easier for you to let him know those innermost thoughts—and it will encourage him to help you overcome those inhibitions.

As you will see when you "wake up."

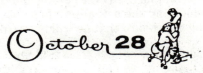

Place your hand, palm down, on a brightly colored piece of paper and use a pencil to draw the outline of the open hand. Cut this out and make five duplicates. Use a tiny bit of adhesive to fix one hand over each of your breasts, one over each of your buttocks, and one over your vagina. Make it look as if the hands were grasping you.

Cover these with tiny, transparent panties and bra, and then put on your sexiest outfit. Have music with an erotic beat playing when he arrives, and offer to do a strip for him. Let your body undulate suggestively as you shed your outer clothing, panties, and bra; and then stand with your legs parted, your eyes closed, and let your hips churn slowly, just as though the hands covering the vital parts of your body were real ones drawing you toward the penis of an unseen lover. It is a very suggestive dance, tempting to any man, and soon you will feel his hands taking the place of those you cut from paper.

October 29

Have a sex dream tonight!

Wearing only your most alluring bra and panties, and lying in a spot where he is certain to walk in and see you, pretend to be asleep when he arrives. Have one hand resting over your clitorial mound and lazily, sleepily begin to move it as he stands watching. Stroke yourself, as if you were masturbating, and whisper his name in sultry tones. Let your hips move until you feel the touch of his hands, and then tell him you were dreaming about him. What follows will seem like a dream!

October 30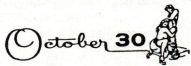

His prowess as a lover is just as important to him as it is to you, and a little harmless exaggeration on your part can actually cause him to perform better than either he or you might expect.

So fib to him tonight!

After you have finished making love, and while he still holds you and has his penis in you, begin telling him how wonderful it was, how he made you feel more feminine than ever before, and tell him how many orgasms you had, doubling the actual number!

You will be setting a standard that he will try hard to surpass in the future.

October 31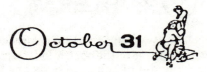

Give him the total oral experience!

Tonight, with no warning and no foreplay to arouse him, let your fingers suddenly free his penis from his shorts, and then kneel to take it in your mouth while it is still flaccid. It won't stay that way long.

Cover as much of it as you possibly can with your parted lips, letting him grow to erection within your mouth, and use every oral technique you know—kissing, licking, and sucking—to fellate him to his climax.

Not only does the growth to erection, while inside your mouth, give him sensations of pleasure no other act can give, it also allows you to gradually adjust to his increasing size and hold in your mouth far more of his penis than you might otherwise be able to accommodate.

November 1

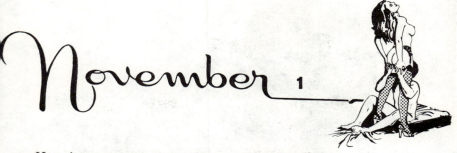

Here is a sure way to take his mind off the TV.

Shower, and then cover your glowing body with a robe thick enough to conceal your nakedness, and take a seat at one end of the sofa. When his favorite show comes on, coax him into lying with his head on your lap, a relaxing position all men love.

Wait until he becomes deeply engrossed in the show. Then slowly, not saying a word, part the front of your robe, so that it no longer lies between your naked flesh and his head. The slight movement will, of course, cause him to turn.

And the sight that greets his eyes will cause him to completely forget the TV!

November 2

Want to find out what really excites him? Then try asking him a few simple questions, but in an unusual context.

Ask him what sexual experience he believes is the most exciting to a woman. Tell him to try to imagine, if he can, that he has suddenly been transformed into a female; then ask him to describe, under those circumstances, the sexual experience he believes would be most enjoyable.

You may be surprised by his answers, but of one thing you may be sure: The sex acts he mentions are really descriptive of ones he would like to share with *you*, under the present circumstances, with no changes needed.

So share them'

November 3

Positions for oral sex are almost countless in number, and each new position adds its own special excitement to the act. Try this one tonight,

and see how he quivers with passion as his erect penis slips deep between your lips.

Lie on your back, nude or semi-nude, with your back resting against the headboard of the bed, so you are in a half-sitting position. Draw him over you, but then, when his legs are astride your body, slip your hands behind his buttocks and guide him into a kneeling position, so that his penis is directly in front of your face, his testicles against your upper chest. Begin to fellate him.

You will find that this position allows his hips to pump freely, driving his erection in and out of your mouth; and your hands on his buttocks, and at his anus, will please him still more.

So why not give it a try?

November 4

He takes both pride and pleasure in bringing you to orgasm after orgasm, you know, so why not make this delectable chore much easier for him?

Shortly before he is due to arrive, strip away your clothing and use your fingers or a vibrator to masturbate until you are on the very brink of orgasm—then force yourself to stop.

Be sexily and scantily dressed when he arrives, and go quickly into his arms. He will soon be aware of your urgent need, will take steps to fill it, and the first thrust of his penis will have you thrashing in his arms.

And so will the next and the next and the next. . . .

November 5

A little jealousy may be good for him—and for you.

Arrange for a girl friend to call you on the phone while he is there. Whisper intimately into the receiver, doing your best to convince him you are arranging a meeting with another man. Continue this until he appears ready to lose his temper, then hand him the phone.

At the worst your little hoax may cause him to turn you over his knee and give you a spanking, which will, in turn, cause the hand that spanks your bottom to begin touching your buttocks with contact of an entirely different nature.

$\mathcal{November}$ 6

Christmas in November!

Call him at work, tell him you are celebrating Christmas early this year, and that you have a very special present for him.

Let him arrive to find you wearing a broad red ribbon that is wound over the tips of your breasts, across your hips and buttocks, and ends in a large bow over your pubis. Have a tag bearing his name hanging from the bow.

Then let him unwrap his present.

$\mathcal{November}$ 7

Give him the ultimate in flattery tonight!

After you have finished making love, and while you remain in his arms, tell him you had never experienced orgasm till you began making love with him. Don't worry about the left-handed reference to other lovers. Men no longer expect every woman to be a virgin, and nothing you can say or do will bolster his ego more than this single statement, whether it be false or true.

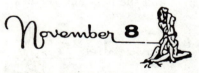

$\mathcal{November}$ 8

Some of the best sex positions are those in which the mobility of the lower body is limited, and it is that type of position to which you are going to introduce him tonight.

Have him lie on his back, his penis erect, while you kneel over him with your face toward his feet. Ease yourself onto his penis, and then, when it is deep inside you, shift your legs so they are extended over his. Press one hand over your upper vagina, to keep his shaft from slipping out, and lie back against his chest. Then once again bring yourself to a sitting position. Each time you lean back, you will discover his penis is slowly withdrawn; and each time you resume the sitting position, the full length of it will be yours to enjoy.

November 9

Pretend to be high tonight!

Roll your own cigarette, using a dark paper, and singe one end of it. Leave it where he will find it, and let him find you gay and laughing, as if you had been smoking marijuana. Tell him you were researching the rumor that marijuana is a mild aphrodisiac, and have him assist you in your research before laughing and telling him the truth.

November 10

He performs cunnilingus not only because it pleases you but because he also enjoys the act, and there are many things you can do to increase his pleasure. Simultaneously fellating him is one, and is the most common, but here is another.

With your panties and bra removed, and with him lying on his back, place your knees beside his shoulders, your vagina over his face, then lean down, exactly as if you were going to fellate him.

Capture his penis between your breasts, as you feel the first lapping of his tongue, then rock slowly back and forth as he continues to lick you. As your moistened vagina moves over his face and your soft breasts move over his penis, you will find his tongue probing deeper than ever before. And your own excitement will be equal to his!

November 11

Buy a sexy outfit that is three sizes too small for you, one that hugs every hollow and curve of your body. Though such an outfit is utterly useless for public wear, you will discover—when he arrives to find you wearing it—that clothing that bites into the soft flesh of breasts, thighs and buttocks has a great deal of erotic appeal. And don't worry about the lack of comfort.

You won't be wearing it long!

November 12

Tic-tac-toe is a pretty dull game, isn't it?

Not when it is played on the naked body!

Challenge him to a set of eleven games, alternating the writing between your body and his, and use watercolors and soft teasing brushes to do this writing. Set a penalty the loser must pay.

And since you will have to remove those watercolors, why not have the loser make payment in the shower?

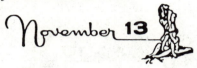

November 13

The mutual enjoyment of cunnilingus can be increased in many ways, and there are many ways in which it can be used as an invitation to an exploration of other sexual avenues. Try leading him down one of those avenues tonight.

After indicating to him that you are eager for the touch of his tongue, and after your panties are removed, lie flat on your stomach with your legs thrown wide. Have him lie prone between your thighs, and lift your pelvis only enough to let him reach your vagina with his probing tongue.

Many men prefer to perform cunnilingus from this position, and as he presses his face against your soft and weaving buttocks, he is literally invited to spread those soft mounds and explore your anus with his tongue—or with his penis.

You will also discover that this position places the soft flesh of your *mons* flat against the bed, letting the gyrations of your body add to the pleasure his tongue provides, and that pleasure will be made evident to him as he tastes the juices of your orgasm.

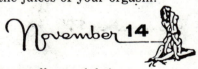

November 14

Be a gypsy fortune teller tonight!

Lead him into a serious discussion of palm-reading. Tell him you have long been interested in this art, and ask him to let you read his palm. Take his hand in yours and teasingly trace the lines of his palm; then tell him, in your most serious voice, that he is destined to lead an incredible sex life. Then place his hand over your breast.

The two of you will soon be making your forecast come true!

November 15

Sew two zippers, or have them sewn, into the front of a blouse. Place one zipper over each breast, and have the openings large enough to allow your breasts to be totally revealed when the zippers are parted. Wear this blouse and no bra.

He will quickly learn the functions of these zippers, and he will tug them down to display your breasts at their tempting best. Naked breasts and a clothed body have the same erotic appeal as a bra that fails to cover the nipples, and tonight his lips will cover your breasts more greedily than ever before.

And they are not all he will cover!

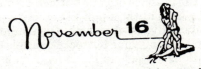

November 16

Give him a tremendous oral experience without taking him fully into your mouth!

Tonight, when he is naked and ready, drop to your knees beside him instead of in the front. Cradle his erect penis in one hand and, leaning forward, close your lips over the side of his shaft. Let them cling lightly to his flesh, applying just enough pressure to cause the outer skin of his penis to move as your lips move, and turn your head from side to side. Extend the tip of your tongue and repeat the motion, letting it curl wetly underneath his penis; and use your hands to stroke his buttocks and testicles.

And be prepared to enjoy yourself when he lifts you from your knees and begins showing his gratitude!

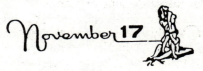

November 17

Write a love letter from him to you!

Put yourself in his place as you describe all the things you have done together, the good moments you have shared, the things you do to give him sexual fulfillment; in other words, write a letter listing all the reasons you have given him for loving you.

The reasons may not be as many as you previously thought, and the writing of this letter will help you see your relationship from a new perspective.

Now tear up the letter and spend the night giving him some additional reasons for loving you!

ℕovember 18

Anal intercourse may not be to your liking, or you may fear that it would be painful, but there is a way you can use analism as a form of foreplay he will love, stopping short of actual entry, if that is your wish. Try it tonight.

Let him remove your panties and, while still standing, turn in his arms. While he strokes and fondles your breasts, reach down and place the tip of his penis in the cleft between your buttocks, so it just touches the anus. Now flex the muscles of your buttocks. You will find they are very easy to tighten around the tip of his erection, and that doing so arouses him magnificently. By moving his penis so the tip of it points toward the floor and flexing your buttocks over his erected shaft, you can vary the sensations he feels in his loins. And as his hands stroke your naked body, his hard flesh teasing your anus, the sensations filling *your* loins may lead you to decide that anal intercourse should not end with foreplay.

ℕovember 19

Let him give you a pedicure!

Your legs are two of your most beautiful sexual assets, and tonight you are going to increase his awareness of them. Wear a very brief skirt, your sexiest panties, and be at your most seductive as you coax him into helping you with your toenails. Let him sit on the floor right in front of you as he does this.

You will, of course, have to lift first one foot and then the other as he works, and he will find it necessary to use his hands to help support your legs; and soon both his hands and his eyes will be moving higher on your legs, closer and closer to the delectable view you present.

You can finished the pedicure another night.

ℕovember 20

Tonight introduce him to a position for rear-entry intercourse that will greatly enhance the pleasure for both of you.

Instead of kneeling while he enters your vagina from the rear—or standing and bending over, as you might normally do—lie flat on your stomach, your legs thrown wide, while he lies over you.

When his penis is in you and moving, draw your legs together, then once again throw them wide, in a scissoring motion that you repeat time after time. Each move will be felt in his penis.

And each stroke of his penis, with the weight of his body pressing your clitoral mound against the bed, will be felt with doubled intensity in the quivering depths of your vagina.

November 21

Make love by candlelight!

Have several candles burning in the bedroom when you enter it, and douse all the other lights. He will soon be in the proper mood.

If you think having dinner by candlelight is romantic, just try to imagine how he will react when he sees the flickering light from those candles dancing over the lush curves and hollows of your body.

But don't just imagine it—do it!

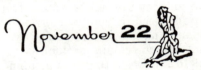

November 22

Try this teasing little movement while having sexual intercourse and see how it excites both of you.

As the two of you begin making love, have him assume the male-dominant position and enter you from the front. As his hips begin to move and his penis withdraws, reach down and circle the shaft of his penis with the fingers of one hand. Hold him so that only the tip of his penis rests in your vagina, the shaft of it in your fist, and slowly move it in circles. Let him pump his hips a few times, pulling your hand away as he does, and stop him to once again move the tip of his penis in those tight circles.

Soon you won't be able to stop him.

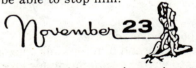

November 23

Ask him to participate in this experiment in awareness.

Sit facing each other, holding hands, and talk about your hopes, dreams, and desires. Begin touching various parts of his face and body, and encourage him to touch yours. Continue talking as you do this, making the conversation as uninhibited as possible, and then begin undressing each other.

Still looking into his eyes, and still talking about things of an intimate nature, begin touching his naked body. Let his hands explore all of your flesh—but keep him talking.

The simple act of touching, you will discover, encourages both of you to speak with a revealing frankness that adds a new and lasting beauty to your relationship.

And it may also arouse you so greatly that you will decide to try a few of the things about which you have been talking.

November 24

Anal intercourse is, to many men, the most exciting form of sex. But there is a way that it can be made even more exciting, so why not give him this immense pleasure tonight?

After lubricating the anus with Vaseline or K-Y jelly, assume a kneeling position and let him enter you. After his penis is fully sheathed in the tight flesh of your anus, reach back between your thighs with one hand and gently clutch his testicles, and whisper to him that you want him to remain motionless.

Now slowly rock to and fro, letting your gripping anus move over the hard shaft of his penis, and each time you reach the point where only the tip of it is held in your flesh, let your fingers tighten around his testicles.

He will love the luxury of having your clinging flesh slide over his motionless penis; and you will find that this is perhaps the most enjoyable form of anal intercourse, because it allows you to control the speed and depth of penetration.

November 25

Show him how possessive you are!

Tell him you mean to brand him for your own, and then do this by using food coloring to write your name on his erect penis. Then show him that you are not really possessive by leaning down and using your lips and tongue to wash away the letters.

He will gladly let you possess him after that.

November 26

Lie with your head in his lap while watching television.

Be wearing a very short skirt or dress, and have on tiny, transparent panties, or wear none at all. Cuddle up to him, drawing your knees up and baring your behind, but wait for him to make the first move.

Unless his hands begin to wander, your naked (or nearly naked) bottom will go unnotcied until the first time he rises from the sofa.

But when he sees what has been so readily available to him during the time he wasted on television, he will quickly make up for the delay. Cuddle up to him as he does so.

November 27

Here is a tremendous position for sexual intercourse!
Why not try it tonight?

Have him kneel in an armchair, with his thighs together and his buttocks resting against his heels. You spread your legs wide and, facing him, grip the back of the chair while placing your knees beside his feet.

You will need to swing your pelvis both in and down to settle your vagina over his erect penis, but you will find that the need to strain slightly in order to gain the full length of his shaft adds a special element of joy to the act. This is in addition to the joy the two of you will receive as he strokes and caresses your conveniently placed breasts.

November 28

Have a balloon race tonight!

Buy about two dozen balloons. After inflating them, tie several to a string long enough to go around your body at the level of your breasts. Make another string to go around your waist, and still another to go around your lower hips. Take off all your clothing and fix these balloons around your naked body. Meet him at the door wearing only these balloons, and hand him a pin.

The race is on!

November 29

Tonight is the night to give him a very special oral treat.
After the foreplay has brought him to pulsating erection, and as he

stands to remove the last of his clothing, drop to your knees, your breasts teasing his thighs, and lovingly take his penis into your mouth.

As your lips move softly back and forth over the length of his shaft, grasp his buttocks with your hands and urge his hips into a pumping motion, thrusting his penis forward to meet your slowly moving lips. Wait until he is settled into this movement, then put both arms behind your back and hold your lips motionless to receive his thrusting erection.

By offering him your soft and clinging lips to use as he likes, and with all the speed or slowness he may like, you are giving yourself to him as few women are likely to have done.

You can be sure it is a gift he will never forget.

November 30

Put the latest college fad to work for you!

"Streaking" is the latest craze to sweep the college campus, and what is fun for the college kids can be fun for you. In this fad, a boy or girl strips completely naked, then goes dashing down a public street—much to the astonishment of those passing by. It is for the shock value that it is done.

Laugh as you casually tell him about this latest college fad, then give him an hour or two to forget the conversation. Go into the bathroom and remove all your clothing, and watch his eyes bug out as you go "streaking" toward the bedroom.

You can bet he will come streaking after you!

December 1

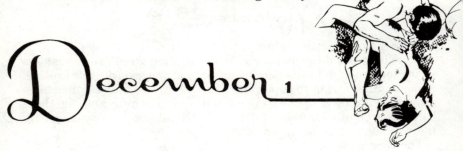

The thick cord that runs the length of the underside of his penis is perhaps his most important erogenous zone, and there are many ways you can use it to give him pleasure. Tonight use it to give him greater pleasure than he has ever imagined!

After he is naked and your panties are off, have him lie on his back.

Move over him, placing one knee on each side of his body, and take his penis in your hand. Press his penis against his stomach, so the tip of it is pointed toward his face, and lower your body over it, letting your labia—the outer lips of your vagina—settle over the underside of his shaft.

Now, leaning forward, move your hips back and forth, letting the delectable hot moistness of your vaginal flesh glide over that sensitive area of his penis as you kiss and caress. Use this as a prolonged prelude to oral sex, to sexual intercourse, or even to bring both of you to orgasm, as can be done, and you will find that he loves this technique as much as he loves you.

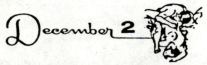

December 2

Here is an exercise in sensuality that involves a mental process rather than a physical one, and is designed to improve your relationship by making it possible for you, at any given moment, to slip into a sexual frame of mind. Try the exercise today, and practice it often.

1. While he is present, try to recall the most enjoyable sexual experience you have known.

2. Let your mind dwell on the memory, trying to create once again the sensations and emotions you felt, and see if you can arouse yourself to a point where your nipples are erected, your vagina growing moist.

3. Try to imagine the way those erogenous zones tingle as he touches them with his tongue and lips.

4. Stare at him as you use these mental processes, and see how it helps.

Sensuality is, in large measure, a state of mind. The process outlined above will help you achieve that state of mind, and you may be surprised to discover that it makes you more attractive to him.

So why not put this exercise to work?

December 3

Does he despise the junk mail that clutters his mailbox, as most men do? Why not cheer him up by adding your own "special offer" to those the mailman delivers?

Write him a brief love note, mentioning one or two of the better moments you have shared and concluding with a sexy "special offer" that only you can make. Seal this in an old third- or fourth-class envelope and add it to the daily pile of sales solicitations.

Then stay close to make sure he doesn't throw it away with true junk mail.

December 4

Show him how your tongue alone can bring him to climax!

As he lies naked on his back, bend or kneel over him and take his penis in your hand. Draw the foreskin down as far as it will go, baring the sensitive tip of his penis, and hold it there. Don't let your fingers move over his shaft, as you might normally do, for tonight your tongue, and only your tongue, is going to being him to explosive ejaculation.

Begin by touching the tip of your tongue to the glans tip of his penis, then letting it flick across this sensitive part of his flesh. Take the very tip of his penis into your mouth, press your tongue against it, and then swirl the tongue over it. Move the tongue clockwise, then counterclockwise. Vary the speed.

Try whipping your tongue across the thick cord that runs the length of the underside of his penis, and lower your face to lick at his testicles. The spewing eruption of his semen may be slow in coming, but the climax will be one he is not likely to forget.

December 5

Time to start your Christmas shopping.

Only you can know the gifts he wants and needs, but try to make at least a few of them very personal, intimate, and reminders of the relationship he shares with you. Then, in addition to these gifts that only you can choose, buy him a pair of slippers, wrap them yourself, and include a note telling him you have reserved a place for them beneath your bed.

December 6

Dare him not to get an erection.
Then make him get one!

Be joking in your manner as you make this challenge, but totally serious after he accepts. Don't touch him with your hands, but have him sit watching as you slowly, sensuously strip away your outer clothing to reveal your scantily clad body. Let the bra follow, and pluck at your nipples until they are stiffly erected. Roll your panties down to reveal a bit of pubic hair, and stroke your thighs with outstretched fingers, your body slowly writhing.

Soon he will admit defeat.

And the proof of his defeat will be your reward for winning!

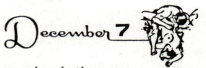

Ask him to take you ice skating.

Wear a brief costume that flatters your legs and buttocks, and be as clumsy as you possibly can, falling against him, letting him support you with strong arms. Take each opportunity for contact—and there will be many—this sport presents.

Soon he may be hot enough to melt the ice!

Tonight present your breasts in a way most men find extremely enticing!

After the two of you have engaged in heated foreplay, and as you prepare to make love, tug the cups of your bra down under your breasts instead of removing it. The bra will lift your breasts, causing them to jut forward and offering them to his mouth, and the slightly disheveled look this gives you will be exceedingly arousing to him.

What follows will be exceedingly arousing to you!

Ask him to see which of you can create the most erotic snowman (or woman). Your artistic attempts may be laughable, but the moments you share in such playful activities will be well spent; and you can encourage the play to take a sexual turn by sneakily dropping a bit of snow under his collar, thus forcing him to retaliate by trying to get a hand under your clothes.

If there is no snow available, make the same challenge but do your sculpting in the sand at a deserted beach or playground. It is results, not materials or location, that are important.

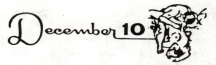

Ask him if he believes in ESP, then ask him to try this experiment in thought communication. It will cause his thoughts to take some very interesting directions.

Have several blank index cards on hand. On each card write a brief description of a sexual act, possition, or technique the two of you enjoy. Shuffle the cards and let him select one at random.

While he concentrates on the description written on the card, you try to pick up his thoughts. Strange as it may sound, many couples who are close do seem to have an odd ability to do this. But that is really unimportant. What is important is that soon he will suggest that you stop thinking about those techniques and start doing them.

Surrender to his powers of suggestion.

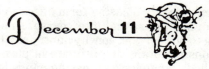

Anilingus, the oral stimulation of the anus, is one of the most exciting things you can do to him. Its one drawback, however, is that, in most cases, the anal stimulation alone is not enough to bring him to climax.

Tonight, though, you are going to combine this stimulation with another, and the combination is going to have him shuddering with delight long after the act is completed.

Lie on your back, with your breasts naked, and have him kneel above you, facing your feet, much as if the two of you were going to perform simultaneous fellatio and cunnilingus. Have him move his body a little bit lower, so the shaft of his penis lies in the cleft between your breasts, and use your hands to press your breasts together.

Now lift your head and let your tongue lick wetly over his buttocks, flickering closer and closer to his anus and finally thrusting against it.

You will soon feel his penis begin to slide back and forth between the soft mounds of your breasts, and soon his semen will be spewing hotly onto your stomach, as he leans down and locks his mouth over your vagina.

December 12

Show him how wild your desire can be!

Tonight, after making love, hold him tenderly in your arms and let him fall asleep. Wait until you are sure he is sleeping soundly, and then, doing your best not to wake him, take his penis in your hand and tease it to renewed hardness. Try to insert it in your vagina without interrupting his slumbers, and let the moving clinging flesh of your loins over his be what causes him to open his eyes.

To find himself being taken by a woman in this manner, with no prior effort or encouragement on his part, is incredibly exciting and flattering to a man, and you will feel him express this excitement with a pulsating and deeply thrusting erection.

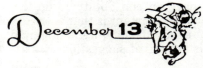

December 13

Fellatio is a tremendously pleasing form of sex. A good position can increase your enjoyment of sexual intercourse. Anal stimulation can be highly arousing to both of you, so why not try combining many techniques and positions to obtain the ultimate in pleasure?

Begin by using body language and teasing hands to guide him into a position suitable for simultaneous oral sex, and stay in this position until the kissing and sucking of your lips has brought him to the brink of orgasm, or until he has done the same to you, and then pull away.

Assume a position for intercouse, have him enter you, and wait until his thrusting penis has both of you ready to climax before once again pausing to change positions. Continue in this manner for as long as possible, and the resulting orgasm will be one well worth the wait.

December 14

Here is one of the better standing positions for sexual intercourse. Why not try it tonight?

When he is hard and ready, stand close to him and slip your arms around his neck, letting him feel your breasts against his chest. Lift one leg and lock it around his, then urge him to place his hands under your buttocks, lifting you. Cling to him until you are settled onto his penis, then place your hands on his biceps and have him grasp both your arms.

Now lean back slowly, with his hands on your arms for support, and then have him raise you back to your former position. You will find that this draws his penis very slowly through your vagina, and not too many repetitions of it will pass before the two of you are purring with delight.

December 15

Do you recall those wasp-waisted corsets that were once worn by most women? The ones with drawstrings that could be used to adjust the fit? They are still available at most large stores, and they can be a very exciting piece of bedroom wear.

Pick up one today, and surprise him by wearing it into the bedroom tonight. Have it adjusted so tight that the domes of your breasts are forced upward and the edges of it make deep creases in your flesh.

This binding of the flesh of the female body is very arousing to most men, and you may find him wanting to draw the garment even tighter over your breasts and thighs before stripping it away and making love.

This is not a garment you will want to wear every night, but it can be a pleasant surprise for him. Why not give it a try?

December 16

Anal intercourse is often more enjoyable to the man if he can perform it while standing, and this position is even more exciting to him because of the way you present yourself for his entry.

After applying lubricant to the anus, kneel in an armchair and steady yourself by gripping the back of it. Then lift your knees and place them on the arms of the chair. Lean forward and raise your buttocks high, and you will be poised at exactly the right height for his entry.

As he uses his hands to grip your buttocks, spreading them still farther for his entry, try to relax the anal muscles. Then, after he is in, use your grip on the back of the chair to steady yourself as you rock back and forth to meet the thrusts of his penis; and let your buttocks undulate slowly before him, adding even more pleasure to what he will be receiving from your tightly gripping anus.

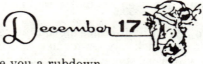

December 17

Ask him to give you a rubdown.

Then give him one he will never forget!

Have him use a creamy body lotion to massage your naked body, and then have him remove his clothes so you can do the same to him. Have him lie on his back and pour the body lotion into the palm of your hand, then reach down to grasp his penis.

Holding his growing erection in your hand, throw yourself over him, your lips meeting his and your tongue darting into his mouth, and let your hand begin to masturbate him.

The creamy lotion will add greatly to the excitement caused by your fingers, and that caused by your naked body writhing against his, and soon he will be eager to have more than just your fingers around his penis.

December 18

Do you know the one secret for making the act of cunnilingus more enjoyable for him? You certainly should, as your own pleasure will increase along with his. The secret is eager participation on your part.

The female who remains totally passive during this act actually discourages the efforts of her lover, while the woman who takes an active role can excite him to new levels of effectiveness. Become a more active and enthusiastic participant tonight, and be prepared to receive an oral performance you never thought possible.

Make it clear to him that you would like him to perform cunnilingus, either through the use of body language or by simply telling him.

Lie on your back and let him take a position between your thighs, then lift your feet and place them on his back. As his mouth approaches your vagina, use the first two fingers of one hand to spread the soft outer lips for his tongue, and place your other hand on the back of his head, urging him to you.

As you feel the first flicking of his tongue, let your feet beat lightly against his back, your pelvis roll; and *tell* him, time after time, how much you love what he is doing.

There is no surer way to make him want to do it time after time.

December 19

Style his hair for him.

Be wearing a very sheer blouse and no bra when he arrives, and have your own hair styling equipment laid out on the kitchen table. Tell him you saw a new hair style you think would look terrific on him, and coax him into letting you try to style his hair that way.

As you go to work, let your fingers caress his scalp, his neck, and his face, and let your breasts brush repeatedly against him. Use the pretext of combing his hair as an excuse to hold him against your bosom, and soon he will be too aroused to sit still for the styling.

Which was what you really wanted, because you love him just as he is.

December 20

Show him how much you want him with you!

Tonight, shortly after his arrival, using any deception that is required, get his car keys away from him. Then try to get his mind on other matters, letting him forget about the keys.

When he first mentions leaving, pout a bit and try to coax him into staying. Then, before he really has a chance to decide one way or the other, smile sexily and drop his car keys down the front of your bra. Dare him to retrieve them.

He will, with quite a bit of fumbling, but he will quickly change his mind about putting those keys to use.

December 21

Try this exciting bit of foreplay tonight.

When the two of you have undressed and are preparing to make love, stand facing him and take his penis in your hand. Step very close to him and place the erected shaft between your thighs, holding it so it is teased by the soft hair of your pubis.

Slip your arm around his neck, letting him feel your erected nipples against his chest, and slowly move your pelvis back and forth, your vaginal hair and flesh teasing his penis. Tighten your thighs against his shaft, let them relax, then tighten them once again.

Now place one hand on his buttocks and use pressure to encourage to him to thrust his penis, and use your other hand to hold his penis so that the hard shaft just touches your vaginal flesh.

But allow him only a few moments of this and then get him into bed, because this is stimulation no man can tolerate for long!

December 22

Here is a position that will make this night live in your memory for many months to come. And it will live even longer in his.

When the foreplay has brought the two of you to the point where further dalliance is unthinkable, have him lie on his back, with his legs close together. Place one knee on each side of his body, just above his waist, so you are facing him, and slowly ease yourself down onto his erection.

When the full length of his shaft is in you, take his hands in your own and raise them to your breasts, moving them over the soft mounds while slowly grinding your vagina against him. Let him enjoy this for a moment; and then, still holding his hands, lean back as far as you possibly can. Let your pelvis roll while leaning back, filling the two of you with incredibly delightful sensations, then use your grip on his hands to pull yourself erect.

By leaning back time after time in this manner, letting your soft vaginal flesh be drawn over the length of his penis with almost agonizing slowness, you will soon have his hips churning upward to hold you joyfully suspended on his gushing penis.

December 23

They say the way to a man's heart is through his stomach, but there are other routes that are much more fun. So why not give him a little of each?

Fix him a sumptuous breakfast (if he doesn't live with you, you can always invite him over), and wear only a skimpy, transparent nightie as you serve it to him.

Lean over him as you serve his meal, letting him smell the fragrnce of your perfume and glimpse the enticing swells of your breasts, and engage in small talk with him as he enjoys this hearty meal.

Then, when the breakfast is finished, touch your lips to his as if to kiss him good-bye. A man is usually most easily aroused during these early morning hours, and as the kiss deepens and his hands begin to wander beneath that skimpy nightie, you will see that he has no intention of saying good-bye for quite some time.

December 24

Christmas eve!

Dim all the lights except those on the Christmas tree. Dress in a sexy gown thin enough to hint at the luscious curves beneath, and be standing with the lighted tree behind you when he arrives, so that your body is clearly outlined for his eyes.

Let him fill his eyes with this tempting view, then make him comfortable on a sofa or chair facing the tree, give him one of the drinks traditional at this season of the year, and snuggle up close to him as the two of you share the warm beauty of the memorable moment.

No setting could be more ideal for romance than this way of sharing this most beautiful of nights, and as one warm embrace leads to another that is warmer still, you will surely find the two of you beginning to glow with a warmth which matches that of the lights on the tree.

December 25

Merry Christmas!

Make it a merry Christmas for him by expressing your pleasure at the gifts he bought—even if they were the wrong size or color, or duplicated something you already owned—and by letting him know how much it means to you to be able to share with him this most love-filled day of the year. This is the traditional day of hope, so let him know that your fondest hope is to spend many more such days with him.

December 26

Many women object to the performance of fellatio because it does not fully satisfy the sexual needs of the female, yet there is a simple technique by which the woman can achieve orgasm while making her oral performance even more gratifying for her male partner.

Why not give it a try tonight?

Have him lie on his back, naked, while you lie beside him with your feet toward his shoulders, your panties off, and your legs parted to give him a clear view of your naked vagina.

As you take his penis into your mouth and begin using all your oral skills on it, lift one leg and place your hand on the soft mound above your vagina. Rub this slowly, your lips still moving over his shaft, and then let your fingers wander to your clitoris. Masturbate as your lips and tongue thrill each nerve in his erected penis.

The stimulation you receive from the oral contact with his penis will make the caresses of your own fingers more enjoyable than you ever imagined they could be; and, if you are like a great number of women, you will derive additional pleasure purely from the exhibitionism and the "naughtiness" this act entails.

As for him, the visual stimulus of watching your fingers caressing your loins will so excite him that his climax will be a tremendous spasm that seems to go on forever.

And it should come at about the same time as your own.

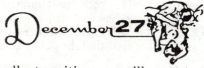

December 27

Here is an excellent position you will want to try.

Have him kneel with his legs close together, and then, facing him, lower yourself down until the backs of your legs are over his thighs, extended behind his body, and settle yourself onto his erection.

Your own weight will cause you to swallow the full length of his penis. By lacing your arms around his neck you will be able to rock back and forth upon it, drawing yourself up until your breasts are pressed against his chest and only the tip of it remains in your vagina; then sink back to reclaim it all. And, of course, his hands beneath your buttocks will be helping you in these motions.

By folding your legs around his body and using the leverage they provide you will be able to vary the rocking motion by sliding yourself slowly back and forth over his penis, and that variation alone is enough to make this position worth trying.

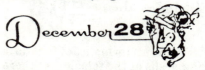

December 28

As a part of foreplay, or as a complete sexual act, try taking this position while fellating him—and watch the glow of excitement spread over his face!

With your bra removed, place yourself on your stomach between his naked thighs, so you are facing his groin. Lift his legs and drape them over your shoulders, at the same time moving up to touch his penis with your lips. Your naked breasts will now be teasing the sensitive undersides of his thighs, his upper buttocks. As you begin sucking and caressing his penis, let your shoulders force his legs higher, and slip teasing fingers beneath his buttocks. Move your shoulders from side to side, causing your erected nipples to sway against him.

The aggressiveness suggested by your position and the touch of your breasts against his sensitive skin will cause him to enjoy your oral skills as never before.

Fulfill his desire for anal intercourse while giving him the ultimate in visual stimulation.

After applying lubricant to the anus (or, better still, after having him apply it), have him lie on his back with his legs together. Take a kneeling position above him, facing his feet, with your bottom poised over his erection. Use both hands to spread your buttocks wide; slowly, very slowly, lower your anus down onto his penis—and listen for his gasp of excitement as he watches his hard flesh slither into your body!

Try this position for fullest enjoyment of sexual intercourse.

Tonight, as you begin to make love, have him enter you from above, in the traditional male-dominant position. Wrap your legs high around his body, your arms around his back, and move with him until his penis is slipping steadily in and out of your vagina; then, locking your lips to his, encourage him to roll to one side.

This facing position allows the two of you to enjoy total bodily contact; it cradles him softly and warmly between your thighs, and gives you far more freedom of movement than you would have with him above you. No position is better suited for slow and leisurely—and utterly delectable—lovemaking.

Enjoy it!

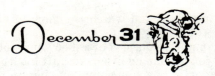

December 31

Throw a party—and make every effort to be alone with him in the crowd. Dance close to him. Laugh over the little secrets the two of you share; and as midnight, the moment for the traditional New Year's kiss, approaches, draw him to a spot where you can really be alone.

Kiss him deeply, let your hand caress him intimately, and describe to him what you intend to do as soon as the party is over. Then smile and add that this is only

. . . The Beginning!